THE
LASCAUX PRIZE
2014

THE
LASCAUX PRIZE
2014

edited by
Stephen Parrish
Wendy Russ

ISBN 10: 0985166630
ISBN 13: 978-0-9851666-3-2

Cover design by Wendy Russ.
Cover art by Mary Qian.

Lascaux Books
www.lascauxbooks.com

Contents

continued next page

Acknowledgements

Special thanks to Peter Dudley, June Geiger, Camille Griep, Paul Liadis, Merry Monteleone, Mindy Tarquini, Jennifer Zobair, and the rest of the cave dwellers at *The Lascaux Review*.

This anthology was funded in part by donations from Carolyn Arntson, Val Beguin, Hélène Cardona, Hope Clark, Susann Cokal, Kathy Fish, June Geiger, Camille Griep, Mary Griep, Alissa Grosso, Heidi Heimler, Michelle Hickman, Sarah Hina, Stephanie Hoye, Donna Hughes, Daniel Johnson, Douglas Johnson, Joy Johnson, Cheryl Kauffman, Angela Kubinec, Sarah Laurenson, James Miller, Mike O'Mary, Jodi McMaster, Chris Rees, Bruce Roush, Audrey Salick, Darrelyn Saloom, Mark Terry, and Jennifer Zobair.

Introduction

One standard we can demand of art is that it deserves to be experienced more than once. Every museum patron has navigated back to a particular wing to view a painting one more time. Every movie buff has watched a favorite again and again. And every dedicated reader has returned to the beginning of a story, sometimes immediately after finishing it, to be transported into its world once more.

As editors of this anthology we were required to read the individual stories, poems, and essays several times, from initial screening to final proofreading. It's a testament to their staying power that we look forward to reading them again when the anthology appears in print.

The Lascaux Review was founded in the spirit of the ancient cave dwellers after whom it was named, visionaries who created not only some of the oldest surviving works of art but of communication as well. The Lascaux Prize seeks to recognize contributions to literature that will stand the unforgiving test of time. We hope you enjoy discovering them as much as we did.

Stephen Parrish
Wendy Russ
December 2014

Ana's Dance

by Donna Miscolta

The windows are open to the blue-black sky, but there is
no breeze to move the heavy air inside the apartment.
Across the street, the diner blinks its electric blue sign.
EAT, it urges. Eat, Ana repeats to herself, only to practice
her English vocabulary, knowing that the craving she feels
is not for food.

She sits rocking, the squeak of the chair chorusing with
the sucking of the baby at her breast. She strokes Carmela's
head as she turns to watch Rudy. He's in front of the bathroom mirror performing—yes, she thinks, performing—
this Saturday night ritual, begun in the months after Carmela's birth.

He's wearing just his underwear. His suit hangs smartly
on the hook of the bathroom door, the stiff creases in the
trousers giving them a look of alertness, as if wary of Rudy's
muscular body. Rudy leans over the bathroom sink, inches
from the mirror. He stretches his upper lip down over his
teeth, snips at the hairs of his elegantly thin mustache, re-

1

tracts his mouth in a smile. He rubs hair cream in his palms, sniffs at its glistening whiteness, and then massages it into his black hair one, two, three times—a calisthenic that works the muscles in the taut curve of his arms and shoulders. He swigs mouthwash from the bottle, and then, posed like a garden statue, spits like a fountain into the sink. With rapid hands, he spanks his face and throat with cologne. Invigorated by the self-administered slaps, he draws himself into his fighter's stance, bounces on the balls of his feet toward his reflection and protects with his left while he delivers several mock blows with his right. Then he whirls to spar with his suit hanging on the door. Prevailing against both opponents, he leaps into the middle of the room, arms raised above his head in victory, and Ana, still watching, makes her mouth smile, while something clenches in her throat.

Perhaps it is indigestion, after all, this feeling that squeezes against her belly and throat, and makes it difficult to breathe.

Heartburn, indeed, had been Irma's mocking reply when Ana had foolishly related her symptoms to her cousin. Irma, ten years older than Ana and married to a silent and featureless gringo, had taken Ana in when she first arrived in Kimball Park. And though Irma had appointed herself chaperon to Ana, following her conduct with a severe eye, Ana had not left the dusty streets of San Blas to be smothered by her cousin's conventions.

Within a few months, she had met Rudy at a Saturday night dance, and in front of Irma's reproving stare, Ana followed the lead of Rudy's smooth, confident steps, responded to the press of his hand at the small of her back as he steered her left or right, answered the cue of his fingertips as they spun her away and then reeled her back in.

In between dances Ana learned more about this dashing young man because Rudolfo Luis Borrego spoke as charmingly as he danced. First of all, he liked to be called Rudy, as in Rudy Vallee, and he crooned an imitation of the singer. He didn't mind being called Rudolph, though, as in Valentino, and he struck a swashbuckling stance. He said he was a painter, and Ana imagined canvasses filled with passionate strokes of color until Rudy laughed and said, no, he painted buildings—tall ones. But his real profession was boxing, and he bounced back and forth on the balls of his feet to demonstrate and then gracefully slid into a foxtrot because, he explained, dancing was an extension of his athletic training. Then he winked, adding that dancing was also romantic, especially with a partner as beautiful as Ana, and he took her in his arms and guided her effortlessly, in command of the music, in command of the other dancers who yielded the floor and the onlookers who watched with both envy and appreciation, and in command of Ana herself who surrendered to the fast-slow-fast-slow sway of Rudy's foxtrot.

As he dresses, Rudy hums the popular songs of the day, inserting words here and there to display the progress of his American accent to Ana, who clings to her Spanish language as if it were a shawl cloaking her from the cold. Rudy wriggles into his jacket to the beat of the song he is humming, and then executes a few dance steps, again with his reflection, this time in the window, the neon blue of the diner sign flashing on his strutting figure.

"I can come if you'd like," Ana offers, though her clothes feel untidy and the pull of Carmela's mouth draining her breast makes her drowsy.

"But Ana," Rudy scolds only half playfully, "you don't like the fights."

He takes it personally that she doesn't like boxing, doesn't see the art in it.

"And besides, what about the baby?"

She holds Carmela up as if to say *our baby.* Rudy steps up, coos at Carmela.

He is delighted as she throws her tiny fists at him and works her mouth in circles bubbly with saliva. "A fighter," Rudy laughs. "Just like me."

She pulls Carmela back. He drops a kiss on the braid wound in a knot at the back of Ana's head.

"Who's fighting tonight?" she asks, as if it matters to her.

"Jimenez and the Turk."

It is not Jimenez and the Turk for whom he dresses so fancy. It is for himself. But as long as he is dressed so prettily, it should not go to waste after the fights, and Ana knows he will stop at the dance hall afterward.

"What time will you be home?"

"Late. Get your rest," he tells her, as if it matters to him, she thinks. He disappears behind the flimsy door of their one-room apartment. But the smell of him lingers on—a

4

bouquet of hair cream, mouthwash and cologne. Ana disperses it momentarily with a sigh.

She listens as his footsteps fade down the stairs, hears the slam of the street door shut them out completely.

She remembers the pound of her own footsteps the day she ran to meet him.

The South City Athletic Club, he had said, importantly, as if it were a famous landmark. Nevertheless, he drew a map on the inside of a matchbook.

When she arrived, she was breathless from the walk, the distance longer than she had counted on. There was sweat at her temples and at the nape of her neck, places Rudy's fingers had grazed as they danced the night before. She dabbed at the moisture on her face with the back of her wrist, lifted her long hair and fanned herself with her hand. She worried about her appearance, how her ruffled hair and damp skin could make her seem careless.

She paused at the door to the gym. There was a sign that she couldn't read, except for the word NO, and this was enough to stop her. She didn't know what to do next. She took the matchbook out of her pocket and looked at it again.

NO had seldom stopped her before. But NO surrounded by as yet mysterious English words made her shy, even with a door. She backed away to look for another entrance that might not have the word NO on it. But once she turned the corner and down the alley, she had to look no further. She came upon a small yard, an outdoor extension of the gym where several young men were engaged in various boxing exercises—punching a bag or sparring with an invisible opponent. Against a low brick wall a collection of women lounged attractively to admire the sleek fighters wholly intent on their workout as if unaware of their audience.

Ana understood that was where she was supposed to go, to sit with the other spectators, but she would not do it. She had not come to this country to be a spectator to someone else's life. Yet she watched. Saw him dance, lithe and quick, evasive when necessary, attacking when he saw an advantage. She waited for Rudy to notice her, and when he didn't, she both fumed and felt forlorn as she turned to walk away. She had just rounded the corner when she heard Rudy call her name. It was almost a bark. And yet she did turn around, because there was a pleading inside his gruff command. She watched him trot toward her in his singlet and shorts, his hands still encased in boxing gloves, the bare portions of his body—his arms and legs and a swath of chest—gleaming.

"Why are running away from me?" he called.

Ana, who believed her life was not about running away, but running toward something did not answer, because she also did not believe in raising her voice in public. Rudy though was not concerned with the eyes that followed him down the street. He's a spectacle, she thought. A beautiful spectacle of a man. So when he asked his question again, instead of saying proudly, I'm not running, I'm walking away, she told him "You were occupied." It came out apologetic (as if she were somehow at fault), instead of reproachful as she meant it to be. But it sent Rudy to his knee and Ana's will to a gentle gust of wind.

She didn't like the actual fights though. Fighting as sport didn't make sense to her. The first time Rudy took her it was to watch a fighter whom he would face in the ring the following Saturday. As Rudy pointed out his soon-to-be opponent's strengths and flaws, Ana could feel the energy of his body, the intensity in his eyes, the readiness in his fists.

Ana closed her eyes each time a fist made contact. She wanted to cover her ears against the urgings of the crowd, through which a grunt or a groan from one of the fighters could be distinguished.

"Next week, you'll see me in there." Rudy said.

He said it as a certainty, and Ana wondered how he knew she would come.

He saved a place for her in the second row, just to the right of his corner, so she would always see him at least in profile. She covered her face at the bell.

She found herself trying to defend the sport to Irma and her husband Donald.

"It's an art," Ana told them. "There is beauty in the movements." She had rehearsed the words that Rudy had so often given her, and though she could say them without error at Irma's dinner table where English was the rule, they sounded flimsy. Weightless.

Weightless is how Ana feels as she sits in the rocking chair alone, Carmela asleep in her crib, in the one-room apartment above the corner market. Here in this California city, the limits of her world are fixed by newspapers that she does not read because the headlines in English baffle her, by street signs that are unfamiliar beyond a few blocks, and by conversations that rush past her undecoded in the aisles of the market downstairs—sounds that are bland and indifferent, like the bread she buys there.

Ana stands up and begins to pace the room slowly, stopping now and then at the window to look beyond the blue sign of the diner to the community hall. All she can see is the roof, but she knows that the windows blaze yellow with light and inside, sweating couples dance as if their lives depend on it. And she knows that Rudy is there, dancing with first one and then another of the partnerless women that line the wall near the punch table, fingering the glass beads at their necks, gazing with practiced nonchalance at the pairs of lilting bodies on the dance floor. As she paces the room, Ana hears Rudy's voice remind her that dancing is essential to his profession in the ring. It keeps his reflexes responsive, rehearses him for a fight.

She continues to walk the perimeter of the room and with each turn she quickens her pace, and as the room begins to shrink she remembers how she used to walk the plaza in San Blas until, finally, she resisted those boundaries, making her way north on a slow, crowded train to end up here in Kimball Park in this apartment above the corner market. And the memory of why she came makes the disturbance she has felt in her stomach disperse to her limbs. It clenches her fists, makes her feet jittery with energy.

Ana lifts the sleeping Carmela from her crib, descends the stairs, lets the door slam shut behind her. She tucks the ends of her shawl around Carmela, though outside the night is warm and embracing. She crosses the street, passes under the cool, blue wink of the diner sign and as she turns the corner to the community hall, she can already hear the music. She enters the hall and pauses, lets her eyes take in the pair of potted palms that curve dreamily at each end of the stage where the band, its members dressed in matching powder blue jackets, delivers a tune brassy with jazz. She scans the dance floor, restless with the undulations of en-twined pairs, and in the middle is Rudy, limbering his mus-cles, timing his reflexes for his next fight, swirling an or-ange-chiffoned brunette, and not yet seeing Ana until she is within an arm's length of him and his partner.

He looks at her with alarm and tries to chase her away with his eyebrows, bushy expressive caterpillars that no matter what their message seem to Ana terribly persuasive. But the bundle in her arms squirms and Ana is embold-ened. She stands her ground. Rudy takes his rumba in the opposite direction. He's ignoring her now, wants to avoid a scene by pretending he doesn't know her. He has so deftly guided his partner that she is so far unaware of Ana and the baby she holds. But now Ana inserts herself in the space between Rudy and the chiffon lady. Before the chiffon lady can react, Ana is thrusting her arms out, displaying the swaddled Carmela who is awake now, her black eyes quizzi-cal, a spit bubble emphasizing the O of her mouth. The chiffon lady recoils and recedes into the crowd around them which has stopped dancing though the music continues. Ana is glad for the music, for the blare of the horns and the crash of the drums, which makes it difficult for any words to be heard. But words are unnecessary. She turns to Rudy who is smoothing his mustache, trying to hide his astonishment at her trespass into his territory. Yet she doesn't claim her dance. Instead she carefully lays Carmela at his feet, at his shoes with their high sheen. She walks away, through the parting, gaping crowd, trusting, knowing Rudy will follow.

*

Rudy always sleeps late on Sundays. He sleeps heavily. There is barely a trace of the cologne he slapped on himself last night before he left, barely a trace of the smells of crowded places—gin, sweat, cigarettes, chiffon-clad ladies. It has been obscured by the stale air of the apartment. By the odor of her own skin.

Ana sits in the rocking chair, Carmela in her arms, and watches Rudy. Outside, the diner sign is unblinking in the daylight. She closes her eyes, alert to the slightest noise, the merest change in temperature, the tempo of breathing.

Ω

Angel and the Day Before
by Matthew Corey

The day before, Angel heard his name called:
"Angel, come here."

He didn't know the man, but the man apparently knew him. There wasn't much that stood out about him. He was tall, had dark hair, dark eyes, and a young looking face. About the same age as his mother.

The school had played videos and spent a lot of time demonstrating how and why kids Angel's age shouldn't talk to strangers. Other than the fact he had no idea who the man was, there wasn't much strange about him. The scenarios at school were so black and white. Ominous music played in the background, a close-up to the man's eyes. There was no close-up here, and no music. Just the normal street sounds: trucks passing by, railroad tracks going down then up. Angel even saw Mrs. Henderson out of the corner of his eye. She was the white woman who lived across the street. He never met Mr. Henderson, but assumed there was one. His mother never had either, and also assumed, but said Mrs. Henderson had been living in the town longest of anyone. The front of her house was almost completely covered in vines, big trees with long branches, and overgrown grass. The front of the house was almost entirely blocked off from the street by all this.

Angel and his friends almost always stopped on their bikes in front of her house whenever they passed. If anything, because they knew she couldn't see. But also for the shade and something about the place begged for something big to happen. But it never did. They would continue their ride around the neighborhood.

She was strange, Angel thought. Other than pushing her grocery cart up and down the few blocks to town once or twice a week, like she was doing now, Mrs. Henderson didn't leave the house. Her odd-colored hair (red or fiery orange on some days) was missing in places. And her eyeglasses or sunglasses depending on the weather were always too big for her face. She never said "hello" to anyone. Sometimes, she nodded at Angel's mother if they happened to be across the street when she left the house. She didn't acknowledge Angel. Maybe she couldn't see him.

Whoever it was talking to Angel, noticed her, too. His eyes showed some familiar amusement. He followed her down the block a bit, then looked back at Angel.

"Is your mother at work today?" he asked. Angel looked at the man's face. His clothes all matched. He didn't dress up, like a lot of the other men in town during the day. He wasn't in a rush like them, either. He wore jeans, a denim shirt, gray t-shirt under it. There was nothing outstanding about them, either. They had a gruff, but tender look to them as well. Like the lines on his face and the warmth in his eyes. Angel nodded.

"Is she in town or at the hospital?" the man asked.

Angel nodded again.

"Which one?" the man said, a little impatient.

Angel hesitated. "Town."

The man pursed his lips. "I thought so. I stopped by there. They said she wasn't there."

Angel looked across the street. The man did, too, but in the other direction. Mrs. Henderson was almost out of sight. She'd made it to the other side of the tracks. She'd be home soon.

"Would you do me a favor?"

Angel looked at the man.

"Would you give her this?" He pulled an envelope from the back pocket of his jeans and held it out to Angel.

Angel had unwittingly taken a step or two back from the man while they talked. Taking the envelope meant taking that step or two towards him again. There was nothing in the man's face that said this was a bad idea. The man looked frustrated, but it didn't seem to Angel he was the cause of it. A small sense of relief, like when the ocean got unexpectedly warm in a cold patch, ran through him as he felt like he wasn't on the spot for once. It wasn't his fault. Somebody else was. Not him. He took the step and the envelope. It was heavier than he expected.

"Thanks," the man said. "And tell her to please answer her calls?"

Angel nodded.

"Does she still work at night at the hospital, too?"

Angel realized he hadn't said much during the exchange. One word at most. His mouth had gotten dry. He nodded.

"Sometimes," he said. The second syllable, though, was more of a squeak. He felt diminished in the man's eyes, and shriveled up.

"Ok. Take that home, please. Don't walk around with it, or go playing with your friends. You enjoying the summer?"

Angel nodded.

"Go on any trips?"

He shook his head "no."

"Is your sister Ok?"

Again, Angel nodded. He began to feel a pressure in his head, like when a basketball or soccer ball had hit him in the nose. Maybe it was from standing in one place for too long. Also, when he stepped back from the man, he inadvertently stepped in the way of the sun, from which there was no relief. Before, the man's face was blocking it. Angel cupped his eyes with his free hand and said:

"Yes."

"You take care of her?"

Yes, he nodded.

"Where is she now?"

He shrugged.

"With your mother? A friend?"

Angel really didn't know.

"Ok," the man said. "Be seeing you. Remember—no walking around with that. Go right home. Please."

Angel kept his hand over his eyes. The man turned around and started walking. He had a kind of hunch around the shoulders Angel hadn't noticed while they were talking. Angel thought about following him for a little, then decided against it. The man was headed opposite the direction of Mrs. Henderson, opposite the way of their house. He didn't turn around either, but just kept walking.

The next day, Angel gave the envelope to his mother. She'd been gone the whole night before, and he didn't want to just leave it somewhere. He kept it in his room all night, hidden by his shoes so she wouldn't see it. Tuesday was her day off and giving the envelope to her interrupted her morning routine. She put the dishes she was washing right down and dropped down on her knees to his level. Asked him where the envelope came from, who gave it to him. Angel didn't answer. It was answer enough for her. She went into the next room where the phone was and called his aunt. They talked everyday and sometimes his mother closed the door so him and his sister couldn't hear. She did that now.

They were supposed to go to the park after lunch. He wondered if that was still going to happen now. When his mother went to close the door, their eyes met for a split second. Angel thought he saw something like fire in hers.

Then, there was just the door. Angel had recognized that look. But not in his mother. It was more like his grandmother. She was a mean woman, and used to live with them. She spoke Spanish all the time, even though she knew Angel or his sister couldn't understand her. When she really wanted to be understood, she hit him. She never hit his sister. And she said "cabron." His mother said "cabron" wasn't a nice word. He remembered the way his grandmother smelled, too, when she lived with them. He hated that about her, too. When she died, his mother was able to work more, take care of her less, and they moved to a bigger house. It had a yard and everything. Still, his mother looked sad after his grandmother died, but he kept how he felt about it to himself. He went into the next room, where his sister played on the rug with a pink house that came apart in the middle and some dolls that were too big to fit in it. She didn't interrupt her playing when he came in the room. He sat on the couch and heard his mother's voice through the wall. She spoke fast, and did all the talking. He couldn't understand a word of it.

Ω

Auspice
by James Silberstein

The bird will tell his future, most likely what his heart already knows. She's gone three days now—to town, or to Mary's, or to some hairy arms—wherever madness goes. But she'll come back.

A crow caws in the distance, too far to know for sure what it's trying to tell him, so he walks the mile and a half to check the mailbox. His footsteps crunch the frozen gravel—the sound, dependable company. The cold mountain air helps him forget. For now, he can pretend the cold is only on the outside. He opens the mailbox to find it empty, except for the rust.

Mistletoe thrives in the stand of oaks across the highway. "Bloodsuckers," he spits. Whenever he sees the parasite, he tries to cut it out with the chainsaw. But it's been too long too late for those scrubs. If left after the kissing, mistletoe kills the tree.

Caw

He spots the black feathers and notes the direction, *northeast*—the crow perched among the ravaged oaks. He knows the time but checks the Omega Seamaster on his wrist anyway, finding comfort in the most reliable thing his father ever gave him. With this data—time, direction, and type of caw—he knows what crow is saying: "*A woman will come.*"

Caw: Later, her pickup will raise dust.

He'll go to the truck to meet her, but he'll wait for her to open her own door.

"I'm sorry," she'll say.

"I know," he'll say, not done believing her.

He'll invite her inside, take her into his arms, and smell her for evidence, the soap not strong enough to cover the sweat from the long drive and the truck's heater, but enough to wash away any other sins he wouldn't want to know about anyway. She won't wear perfume, like a dare to take her as she is.

"You've been chopping wood," she'll say, removing flecks from his hair.

"The splitter is broken. I'll go get a new hydraulic line, tomorrow."

"Maybe it can wait. Maybe we can stay in."

"Maybe."

"It'll be cold tomorrow."

"It will."

"Yes," she'll say.

"I better take a shower, since I don't smell as nice as you."

"No, I like it." She'll move to him.

He'll pull her in, tighter than he should, both of them trying to protect whatever tenderness they have left. They'll barely make it to the bed, her hands tearing at his flannel, pine splinters in its fibers. He'll feel the sticky of pitch between his hands and her skin. Her dress too thin for this weather, even inside by the stove, restraint will give way to heat, yield to fire, until they burn into that moment.

"Soha," she'll whisper, an inside joke from the first time they made love.

"Soha," he'll repeat after her.

They'll lie quiet awhile.

"Did the birds tell you I was coming back?"

"They did."

"How come I never met that old woman?"

"You did your own laundry."

"I couldn't afford to pay an old Tibetan witch to wash my undies."

"She wasn't very expensive."

"Not everybody's daddy leaves them enough money to—"

He'll interrupt her, "Let's not fight."

"I'm not fighting." Her eyes will widen.

Trying to reconcile, he'll say, "Besides, she said she was repaying a kindness from a past life."

"So that's why she taught you to talk to birds, why she transmitted the ka-ka-ka-ka-ka-ja-ka . . ."

"*Kakajarita Sutra.* Please don't mock."

"I'm not mocking. Remember I went to Dharamasla looking for moksha too."

"And you found me."

"It was you seduced me with all those big Sanskrit words."

"You said you were my yogini," he'll say, remembering how her darkness brightened only when he held her.

"You should have known I was a crazy dakini," she'll say, and he'll read the sorrow in her eyes.

"Maybe it's not too late to fulfill our bodhisattva vows."

"Maybe." She'll nestle in to him and they'll fall asleep.

He'll dream of Dhauladhar, the snow-capped range rising out of the Kangra Valley, once a symbol for what he thought he wanted—a far-out place to practice the meaning of the words he learned, *karuna, shunyata, mahamudra.*

For a while they'll sleep soundly on the six acre California retreat, nestled at tree line among the Manzanita and mourning doves.

But Crow knows the difference between dream and reality. After being eaten by its shadow, the bird lost time—present, same as past, same as future. Crow knows what they're capable of, always has, always will.

Caw: He'll wake to hear her tearing up the closet for a lost glove, *karmas* and *kleshas* the conditions for her crazy.

He'll get out of bed to shower. When he's done, she'll still be ransacking the closet. Knowing she won't stop until he says something, he'll ask her to pass him a clean pair of pants.

"You never understand," she'll say.

"But I do."

"Stop it! Stop saying that. You never let me feel the way I do." She'll have stuffed away the dress and be wearing his shirt, too big for her, making her furious action seem inconsequential, comical.

"You're too busy telling me 'I don't understand' to see how I always let you feel however you want."

"I'm so tired of this." She'll leave the closet, strewing clothes behind her.

He'll follow her. "You never give it a chance."

"It's not working."

"You have no faith."

"You don't believe in me."

"We should sit." He'll wave a hand toward the cushions on the floor before the hearth.

"I don't want to."

"Come here."

"No."

"It's not too late *to practice*," he'll hiss through a clenched jaw.

"Means nothing."

"You're wrong." He'll reach for her.

"Don't touch me."

"Stop."

"You don't want me here."

"Just stop it." He'll grab her.

"You've said it before—you wish I would leave."

"Please," he'll say trying to soothe but merely agitating her more.

"Let go!" she'll say, pushing, clawing.

Not sure whether to tighten or release, he'll do both—one hand opening as the other stays tight around her wrist. She'll fall to the floor. He won't let go as she kicks.

The two will scream, never to be doves.

*

Shunyata means *the essence of everything* and Mahakaruna means *great compassion*. And the only thing he's learned out here is how to listen to birds. The black wings flap but refuse to fly.

Seeing no other way, he closes the mailbox and walks back to the events he knows will come. His heart the kind of thing only a crow would eat.

Ω

A West Virginia Walk-up

by David Salner

PD had a vacation day coming and he spent it by winning a goat at the county fair. Exactly how he won it, and whether it was a game of chance or skill, are issues I prefer not to address at this time. As he and the goat were driving home on Route 79, the thought occurred to him—what am I going to do with this goat?

This is not a question he could avoid for long, since he lived in a walk-up apartment. There are more people than you might think who live in walk-up apartments in West Virginia, though very few live in elevator-equipped buildings. Despite this fact, state and county fairs in West Virginia continue to give out prizes of goats, pigs, cows, and horses, as if the West Virginia landlords would be proud to have these hoofed tenants under roof.

The top prize of one county fair was a small herd of American bison, which you can see to this day, grazing on the east side of Route 79, just north of Clarksburg.

The issue of state and county fair prizes is one that probably needs to be addressed, but not by me. Issues of public policy are beyond the scope of my writing ability. One man and one goat is about all I can handle. And so back to PD, who had just begun to understand the dilemma he faced. He exited Route 79 and did what most of us do in the face of these kinds of stumpers. He headed for the nearest bar, which was Johnny's Tap 'n Pool.

As he left his truck in the lot, he warned the goat, "I'm going to have a beer—don't leave the back of my truck."

For PD, this was one of those watershed moments. If the goat heeded his warning and stayed in the truck until he came out, well, then, he might be a keeper. But if he wandered off, PD wasn't going to go looking for him.

The inside of Johnny's Tap 'n Pool was not unknown to PD, but as he sat down at the bar, he couldn't remember if he knew this particular bartender. He certainly didn't know his name. He wondered why he had to win a goat, instead of 50 silver dollars, like the second place winner, or a torch set and a lifetime of propane refills, like third place.

He went over to the juke box and studied the songs, which were listed in tiny print that you could read only by bending over and squinting. The bar was quiet because it was just after noon; night shift had already gone home and the day-shift workers were still wasting their time at work. Also, the fact that Route 50 to Grafton was closed down for resurfacing didn't help. PD had gotten through the barricades only because he knew a shortcut across Homer Massey's lawn.

Finally he found a tune by Willie Nelson, dropped in fifty cents, and headed back to his seat at the bar. He ordered another beer and couldn't remember which song he put on. Was it "Red-Haired Stranger" or "Blue Eyes Crying in the Rain?"

"Juke box is out of order—Give you back a quarter," the bartender said. Because they rhymed, PD at first thought these were the opening lines to the song he had just spent a quarter on. He drank another beer in silence and reached into his pocket for a ten-spot, since he was always generous, especially with tips. Then he realized he'd spent all his money at the county fair.

"Say," he said, and the bartender stared back at him expectantly. "Say," he began again. "I have a goat in the back of my truck that can drink beer from an ashtray."

"I don't care if your goat wrote FDR's New Deal. I'm not wasting any beer on him."

"You wouldn't talk about my goat like that, if you knew he could fix your juke box," PD responded, not missing a beat.

The bartender went off down the bar to pour a beer, because a couple of guys from day shift at the carbon factory had come in. That was the nearest plant to Johnny's Tap 'n Pool. At least the nearest one still running. This part of the country is full of dead plants and dead mines. Some people try to make a living picking up steel and iron left around the old work sites. Each rusty tool might have a story to tell, but it doesn't pay. About scavenging in West Virginia I could say a great deal, and perhaps I will, but on another occasion.

The bartender and the carbon-plant workers said a few words and laughed. PD couldn't hear what they said but his ears burned. They must be talking about my goat, he thought.

When the bartender got back to PD, he said: "OK, your goat fixes my juke box, and I'll let you drink for free to-night."

"Hang on, Buddy, my goat doesn't do any skilled labor for minimum wage."

"Suit yourself. That'll be five dollars for two beers."

"I've got a credit card . . ." PD said.

"Sorry, the only thing I take is cash—or some repairs from your goat."

As PD went out to the truck, he wasn't sure his goat was ready for such a major role. He was almost hoping he wouldn't be there. In that case, he could explain the situation to the bartender, who would certainly be interested to hear how PD spent his last dime at the county fair, buying chances on a goat. Whose heart wouldn't be moved by the story of a man whose beloved pet and valuable prize had just run off?

But the goat was there and turned his big eyes toward PD and licked out of his hand. PD leaned over and whispered something into the goat's ear, and the goat got out of the truck and followed him into the bar.

PD noticed that a couple more day-shift workers had come in from the carbon plant. They all looked at the goat and one of them said:

"Hey, barman, I didn't know you let goats drink in this bar."

"The goat doesn't drink," the bartender shot back. "He only does repairs."

"Just a minute," PD responded. My goat can't do any repairs unless he's had a few beers."

The barman made an unfriendly gesture at PD and walked away to pour some beer.

"That sounds reasonable to me," one of the workers said. "Hell, a goat can't work for nothing."

"Look," the bartender exploded, "I ain't pouring beer for a goat. Does it have any ID? Does it understand English if I read it the warning about drinking alcohol when you're pregnant?"

"I never heard of a Billy Goat getting pregnant," PD responded, handing a clean ashtray to the barkeep. "And my goat only drinks bottled beer."

The bartender acted disgusted, like it was below him to fill a goat's ashtray with beer.

PD put the ashtray down on the floor and the goat sucked it up and everyone insisted that the barkeep pour another one, which the goat also lapped up. The goat looked up, and PD realized from the expression on his face that he had a pet for life.

"And now for the repairs," PD said. "You're going to hear the first lines of either 'Red Headed Stranger' or 'Blue Eyes Crying,' I forget which."

He whispered something in the goat's ear and the goat looked up at him, pawed at the floor like he couldn't wait to do some troubleshooting, and then passed out.

The bartender gave PD a look, like, "If I carved you up and stuffed you in a bottle of vinegar, would you be as tasty as pig's knuckles?"

"Look at my goat, you've slipped him a mickey," PD said, hoping for some sympathy from the day-shift workers. They weren't unsympathetic—just not prepared for the drama that had unfolded before their very eyes. Anyway, they stared blankly from the bartender, to PD, to the goat.

"Damn you all," PD fumed, and kicked at the juke box with his muddy size 12s.

"Blue eyes crying in the rain," came Willie Nelson's quavering voice from the juke box.

Then the carbon plant workers sprang to life, applauding. And more applause broke out with every beer PD downed or every ashtray quaffed off by the goat, who'd woken up as soon as the merriment began. By the end of the evening, the two of them were feeling no pain. At some point during the late night or early morning, PD got the goat back in his truck and then up the three flights of steps to his apartment.

The next morning Felix Younger—the older of the Younger brothers— showed up to give PD a ride to work. It was a well-known fact that Felix resented PD and was just looking for a chance to drop him from the carpool. He hadn't been able to do it because of what everyone else would say, namely that PD was a fine fellow and would never do Felix like that if the shoe was on the other foot. So when PD wasn't waiting out in front of the apartment building at 6 a.m., Felix stormed up the steps to wake him. When he saw two big brown eyes staring out of the covers at him, Felix thought for sure it was PD, until he realized it was a goat.

"PD has a goat for a mistress," Felix told everyone, thinking this time he had PD good.

"How could a Billy Goat be a mistress," PD scoffed at him.

*

The acquisition of a goat did wonders for PD. He started to exercise so as to walk the goat, began cooking regular meals so he could feed the goat leftovers, and took a correspondence course in animal husbandry. To say that the responsibility was good for PD was an understatement, for he completely turned his life around.

Fortunately, the landlord liked the goat, too, and let him stay outside in the yard the rest of the fall. By winter, he and PD finished the basement, which used to be a dark, leaky furnace room. They put a mattress in one corner for the goat to sleep on, but he preferred to lie on a throw rug by the furnace. In a West Virginia walk-up, the best place for a goat to stay is the basement so he doesn't bother the other tenants by clattering up and down the steps.

You're probably thinking that in this case, it was all for the best for a contestant living in a West Virginia walk-up to win a goat. But that was more because of the exceptional qualities of PD and his goat. The general principle that I explained at the very beginning of this piece still stands. Hoofed creatures are not appropriate state or county fair prizes. This is an issue that should be addressed, but not by me.

*

"A West Virginia Walk-up" originally appeared in *Green Hills Literary Lantern.*

Ω

Bedtime Stories
by Justin Campbell

M y father's hands are cracked and ashen. As I serve him a cup of ink black coffee, he examines his fingers and his palms. Lines of cracked white running through his black skin look like a tributary map. I set the coffee down in front of him.

"I'm getting old, *mija.*"

I pull my hair into a ponytail with a brown rubber band. "You're barely seventy, dad."

"I am old, see?" He holds up his hands.

"If you lotioned them like mom used to tell you too . . ."

Any mention of my late mother engenders a kind of awkwardness between us. He sips his coffee and pushes his black-rimmed glasses up on the bridge of his nose. "What are we doing today?"

My father has been living with us for just under a year now. He could not stay with my brother because my brother lives in the closet space of a friend in Santa Monica. "We need to go to Costco and then to Jason's school in the afternoon. I told Miss Stevenson that I'd come and help out."

"And tonight?"

"Carl will be home at seven, we'll eat dinner, and then put Jason to bed."

"So the usual."

"Yes. The usual."

My father immigrated from Jamaica when he was a young man of twenty-three and has spent the entirety of his life in the States supervising a landscaping team. He was the only non-Hispanic man there. Growing up, most of my friends assumed my father wore a white shirt and tie to work like theirs did. Before retiring with two slipped discs in his back, he was often mistaken for being Cuban or Dominican. Clients would say things within his hearing that they thought he couldn't understand. Nevertheless, he became close with the Spanish-speaking crews he worked with. My brother and I grew up being called *mijo* and *mija* and receiving *besos* after he told us bedtime stories at night before sleep shut our heavy eyelids. He would sit on the edge of one of our beds, smelling of the pure, simple soap he showered with when he got home from work. "Tell us a story, papa," I would ask as my brother sighed and pulled the blankets over his head.

My father would close his eyes and take a deep breath. "Okay *mija*. Okay."

*

When I was little boy, not much older than your brother is now, my friends around the neighborhood used to call me *beenie bwoy*. This did not bother me because it was true. I had small hands and short legs. In those days, I used to walk to school through a tall grass field with me lunch money and books, wearing me only school uniform jacket. This field was a kind of short cut for me because on some mornings my mother would send me to the market in Kingston to get soap for her to use to wash the day's dirty laundry. In Jamaica we did not have washing machines like you do today. My mother had to do it with her own two hands. One day, I was running through the field, fixing to be late, when up out of the tall grass came what the folks back then used to call a *bandulu*. His name was Franklin and he was the baddest boy in all of Kingston. The *passa passa* of the boys at school was that Franklin's father did the boy's chores for him and that one time the boy's teacher took five raps on *her* knuckles from the flat side of Franklin's ruler. He usually had a group of good for nothing boys that followed him like a pack of wild dogs. On that day, Franklin was alone, carrying a small knife with what looked to be a sharp blade in his hand.

"Where you going in such a hurry, Winston?"

I tried for to keep on walking, but Franklin slid in front of me for to block me from getting through. "Be off with you," I said. "I'm going to be late for school."

"Why you care so much about these books and *tings*?"

"Just let me go."

He pointed his knife at me. "You got to pay the toll first."

"What you want, Franklin."

He looked my things. "Give me your jacket."

"You wearing the same one."

"I know," he said with a grin. "But me want *yours.*"

The jacket was my prized possession. My mother had to wash and press it every Saturday. I made sure to never get crumbs from my lunch of bun and cheese on it while I was studying at the school. My father would have run my behind ragged if I had lost that jacket, no matter the story I came home a crying with. "Me mum gon' kill me."

Franklin moved closer to me and I tell you now I could smell the rum on that *rude bwoy's* breath. "Franklin be your mommy," he said. "Franklin be your daddy, too." I felt the dull side of his knife on my cheek and knew me had to give him something. "If I give you me lunch money, will you let me be?"

Franklin spun the knife in his hand. "How much you have?" I told him. "Well give it here, then."

I dug into my shorts pocket for the coins and handed them to the boy. He held them in the palm of his hand and counted them with his finger. "Get, before me decides I want your shoes and books too."

I ran faster than ever before and got to the school gates as Richard was pulling the rope to ring the bells for the start of class. Even though I was hungry all day, it only made me more focused on me schooling. Franklin had taken my money, but your father knew that he was winning the war, see? While Franklin was off taking jackets from little boys, I was at school learning, eating at the table of knowledge.

"This is why going to school is a privilege, *hijos.* Many people are not afforded the same opportunities as you are." He would then turn out the light and kneel down at the side of my bed. My brother's breathing would already be thick and heavy and I would stare at the popcorn on the ceiling while my father began his nightly prayer.

*

In Costco, all of the stay at home moms and small business owners are there, crowding the aisles. As I push the over sized cart through the towering shelves of industrial sized containers of ketchup and mustard, my father follows me, his hands placed behind his back like a small town British constable, inspecting the craftsmanship of the deck furniture and the quality of the camping equipment. "You know," he says to me as we enter the fruit section, "your mother could have never shopped for food in a place like this."

"Apples or nectarines?"

"How about mangos for a change."

"They don't have mangos, dad."

"Hmm."

"Apples or nectarines?"

"Nectarines, then."

I grab the sixteen-pack of nectarines off of the shipping pallet and hold it up for my father to see. "*This* is why you came to the states, dad."

He looks down at the plastic container. "But we had good fruits back home."

"Not like this you didn't." I set the nectarines in the basket and push the cart towards the row of checkout lines.

*

At Jason's school, we get nametags in the front office that say "Visitor" on them. My father smiles at Janet, the school secretary, but does not say anything. When we get to my son's kindergarten classroom, Miss Stevenson is in the middle of reading a story about a brown bear and the different colors that it sees. We stand in the back of the room until she is finished and the children are transitioning to group work. Jason waves at us and opens his pencil box. The teacher walks up and greets us with sigh of exasperation. "I'm *so* glad you made it. My room mom for yesterday got sick and I have all these pumpkins that need to be cut out, along with copies of the worksheets that I need made for tomorrow—"

"It's fine," I say with a smile. "I'll take care of it." My father sits down in a chair that is too small for me but perfect for him and we cut pumpkins out of orange construction paper. The teacher walks over. "We usually ask visiting grandparents to read us a story. Would you be willing to do that today?"

I glance at my father. He continues to cut out the pumpkin. The only thing he ever reads is the Bible. He holds up a pumpkin, cut cleanly along the edges of the thick, black lines. "I will read to the children."

The teacher smiles. "That's great. We'll have you do it after these math groups are done."

"That's fine," he says as he starts on another pumpkin.

She leans in towards the table. It's clear from a quick glance down the scoop neck of her blouse that young Miss Stevenson hasn't had to breast feed yet. "I love your accent, by the way."

My father averts his eyes. "That's very kind of you."

When the math centers are done, the teacher calls all the children over to the carpet with the colored squares. She announces that a special visitor has offered to read a story to the class. Jason beams as my father walks to the front of the room and sits down on the stool. Miss Stevenson played volleyball in college so my father's legs are dangling a good foot above the floor. He rests them on one of the rungs. The teacher hands him a book. He opens it to the first page, and for a moment, everything is still. Then, he closes the book with such force that it causes the some of the children to jump. "Have you all read this story before?"

"Yes," the kids say in unison.

He smiles at me. "Then why do we have to read it again?"

The teacher looks at me with concern and I shrug. My father leans forward, his voice low and mysterious. "When I was a lad, a little older than you are here, my friends in the neighborhood used to call me *beenie bwoy.*"

*

"Jason told me you and your dad visited his class today," Carl says, the glow from his iPad turning his face a creamy blue. Carl is reading articles from *Men's Health* and I am reading a book on the Obamas that I checked out from the public library. I stick my finger in between the pages to save my place.

"The teacher asked him to read a story to the class."

"He read something from the Bible?" Carl asks.

"No."

Carl slides his finger across the screen. "Hope he didn't bore them with one of his poverty tales."

In that moment, I hate my husband with his MBA from Chicago, his East Coast private schools, his New York City CFO father and his trophy wife mother. I hate the fact that after almost a year of my dad living with us, my husband is not able to see him as anything more than a manual laborer. "The kids loved it," I say.

"I'm sure they did."

I close the book and swing my legs over the side of the bed.

Carl looks up. "Where are you going?"

"Downstairs, to get some water."

Carl's attention has already returned to his screen. "Ok, then."

I walk past a kitchen lit by the glow of the clock on the microwave and a white light shining from the ice dispenser on the refrigerator. I knock on my father's door. "Yes?"

I poke my head in. "Are you sleeping?"

He is lying in a simple twin bed, his hands placed behind his head as he stares up at the ceiling. "Old men do not sleep, *mija*. They only rest their eyes."

x

38

I enter and sit in the chair under the window.
He sighs. "Well then. Tell me a story, *mija*."

*

"Bedtime Stories" originally appeared in *The African American Review*.

Ω

Brothers of the Salvageable Crust
by Joe Kapitan

Professor Leonard Littmann had just announced Interaction Node 42. With a flick of a switch, the house lights came up in the main auditorium of Townsend Hall. Littmann—middle-aged, adjunct, embarrassingly unpublished —smiled as he scanned the rows of the young women filling the seats. His bed-tanned hands gripped the podium like an unwilling dance partner.

"Consider the conundrum: When is silence louder than communication? When does communication become just a quieter form of silence? My dear ladies, can you see where this confrontation is headed?" asked Littman, pulling at the sleeves of the salmon-colored cardigan tied over his shoulders. "What would you establish as an appropriate response/non-response ratio for Dave as he attempts to face this rather significant setback?"

Dave, whose real name was Rusty, shifted uncomfortably in his steel-toes. The heat thrown down by the spotlights was broiling him in his flannel shirt, frying his bald spot. Littman had never told him anything about any damn spotlights or Interaction Nodes, let alone a theater full of coeds dissecting his every move. But shame on me, Rusty thought, he hadn't asked what to expect when he signed on to play Dave Dithers in Littmann's grad-level course, Sociology 551: Interactive Marriage Simulation, or something like that, he wasn't quite sure of the words, but it was high-level stuff, certainly a bit beyond him. Darlene Dithers, Dave's difficult and sporadically-attractive faux wife, was portrayed by Melanie Grabowski, who was supplementing the income from her other part-time job at Food Services. At that particular moment, Melanie had her head in her hands on the opposite side of their prop kitchen table. She'd just finished delivering the session's agitated Darlene monologue: "Dave (something something) all the empathy of a pipe wrench (something something) emotionally bankrupt and I'm not sure we can even go on from here." Someone in Row G applauded a little. Melanie pounded the Formica tabletop for good measure.

The day's Core Relationship Stressor, or CRS, was part one of a two-session focus on Emotional Unavailability. Previous weeks had been a parade of such manufactured crises as Sudden-Onset Unemployment, Infidelity, the Fertility Clinic Follies, a special double session on Rebellious Drug-Peddling Offspring/School Expulsion right before midterms, then after the break came Sexual Dysfunction,

Internet Porn Addiction, Parasitic In-Laws, and Adventures in Personal Bankruptcy. He and Melanie were two people who had been through hell together and still had yet to go on a real date, courtesy of Littmann's vision. Each semester, Littmann re-staged his particular brand of social theater, and the sororities supplied one coed to help him stem his loneliness in return for advance copies of final essay questions. The designated Littslut bartered them to the rest of the sorority girls (making up eighty percent of the class), who in turn bartered them to the field hockey players, who made up ten percent of the class, who sold them outright to the remaining ten percent composed of various not-It-Girl subcastes in cash-only transactions. "Clicks for Chicks" had been the number-one-most-popular humanities elective at Farmingham College for five years running. It was part institution, part ecosystem. It had its own food chain.

Rusty awaited his cue. Littmann said, "Let's define the choice at this node—does Dave try to emotionally connect with Darlene, or does he walk away? Ready your devices. And . . . interact."

Rusty considered his instincts, followed by the usual distrust of his instincts. He had already fled backstage when the Results Monitor flashed 74% Try to Connect.

*

In the tiny locker area behind the stage, Melanie pulled off the frumpy Darlene housecoat and put on her Food Services jacket, which smelled of pilaf and pine cleaner.

"Have any plans later?" she asked, replacing fuzzy slippers with brown flats.

"Got some mowing to finish before it gets dark," Rusty said, and then wanted to say he was free after that, but he debated that last part with himself a little too long. With a half-wave, Melanie left.

Locker time was what Rusty breathed for, those precious few minutes of transition between Melanie the Stranger and Darlene the Fake Spouse. In the warped little solar system that was Farmingham College, even a misshapen asteroid like him found a few moments of perihelion with objects like Melanie, and when the moments came, he gravitated. Melanie had told Rusty about the solid four years she'd put in at her desk in the catacombs below South Dining Hall, and how she'd already been promoted three times, placed on the fast-track, reaching the level of Deputy Starches Coordinator a whole year early. She was the one in charge of menu logistics for breads, yeasted bread-like baked goods, non-yeasted baked goods (including the whole subcategory of cookies and flatbreads), assorted rices, grains, cereals, and every other week, potato products. She shared potatoes in a mediated agreement with Ingrid Holmgren, the pompous bitch in Fresh Produce who filed a union grievance claiming jurisdiction over tubers. Ingrid's lame argument: that most other tubers, like carrots and beets, are actually starchy vegetables, not vegetablish starches.

And that was always the problem, wasn't it? All the Ingrids and Littmanns and Marty O'Mearas of the world that were just two-legged delivery systems for a slow poison designed to strangle the dreams of guys like him. God, the places he could have gone without them! He pictured a cabin big enough for two in Canada somewhere, perched on the edge of a pine forest, and next to it a large sunny field, and Rusty's half of the field was a 50/50 blend of Kentucky Bluegrass and Red Fescue, neatly mowed in concentric rings, and Melanie's half would be planted in wheat and corn and more types of tubers than that bitch Ingrid Holmgren could ever dream of.

The typical indicators pointed to Melanie pushing thirty, Polish-built, intermittently brunette. And that was just how she described herself, in qualifiers, always in pairs of words like leisurely athletic and Sundayishly Catholic. She tended to let things slip about herself as they sat in front of their lockers and dressed in their Dave and Darlene garb, and when she did, Rusty stopped to feel the magnets banging around inside his gut again, because this was the time for her personal things, heavy and intimate things, shavings from her iron core, like how she pictured her life as a sort of sad rosary—identical concretions of miserable days strung together with a repeating sequence of bad haircuts. Or how no one had ever bought her flowers just for the hell of it. Or how she hasn't had the time for a man, being the only child and thus default caretaker of an obsessive-compulsive hypochondriac mother who insisted on harboring imaginary afflictions in groups of three. Mother Grabowski's current line-up combined a layer of caffeine-induced sleepwalking over a long-suspected urinary tract infection and undiagnosed vertigo. Melanie had been setting her alarm for three in the morning and searching the closets until she found the one Mother G had fallen over and pissed herself in.

Rusty considered square footage once again as he maneuvered the mower deck around the sugar maple saplings next to the Fine Arts building. Success, to him, came in square feet, at least that's how he was raised to think, so he'd been saving up for a place to call his own that would be big enough for someone else to call her own. Again he added together how much he'd need for himself, how much additional for another, say maybe a Melanie-sized another, and how much more for an another's mother. Could he even afford that much? Maybe so, if that another didn't have a lot of junk, and sometimes brought home Tupperware's of excess starches from the dining hall, and if the another's mother was bed-ridden by that time, and pretty much stayed put in a two foot by six foot area, well then just maybe. When he got that place of his—when, not if—then he could land his catch, not just drag a bare hook through water like he'd been doing. Rusty told his boss, Marty O'Meara, all three hundred pounds of Marty, that he was almost ready to move out of the maintenance loft and rent an apartment over in Collegetown, but Marty said yeah, sure Rusty, you'll get a place when I get a treadmill. Marty didn't even own a pair of sneakers. Marty'd never sneaked up on anything in his life, including weather radar.

Rusty shut down the mower deck and fired up the weed-whacker by rote, the same way he sleep-worked and cot-slept and saved his money and avoided temptation as the seasons cycled from plow to mulch to mow to rake. It was the rhythm of the last ten of his thirty years spent keeping up the grounds of The Farmingham College of Liberal Arts. His small set-up in the loft of the Maintenance Building cost him nothing—free cot, free sink and toilet—as long as he agreed to monitor the automated irrigation system after-hours in the summer, and keep the main walks cleared during pre-dawn winter snows. He had a Rec Center pass for showers and his employee discount at the dining hall. He had a couple of co-workers that some might classify as friends, or at least comrades, fellow bare-hook-draggers.

How many times had he and the other grounds crew guys gotten cleaned up at the Rec Center and splashed on some Old Spice and made Ramon promise (in Spanish) to shut his Mexican yap and then went out cruising the chain restaurants up and down the strip, all those Ladies' Nights at Applebee's, but the women in college towns like this were always journal-published or tenure-tracked or research-granted, and when it was their turn to ask him what he did for a living, Rusty mumbled something about horticultural engineering and pretended to feel the vibrations of an incoming call in his front pants pocket, from the deck of cards he pretended was a cell phone, and he said sorry, that's got to be the Smithsonian again, their Civil War rhododendron collection is on life support, and since when am I the only goddamn board-certified stem graft surgeon east of the Mississippi, and ran out the emergency exit.

Rusty drove the equipment back to the Maintenance Building just as the sprinkler heads on the main quad awoke for nocturnal irrigation. Up in his loft, he grabbed a Dr. Pepper from the mini-fridge and stretched out on his cot. He told himself again that he'd have a real bed soon, the kind with a headboard and all, but believed it a little less than he said it, because he still heard little voices sometimes, tiny airline-bottle-sized ones, tink-tinking as they rolled around the vehicle bay, usually right about now, at dusk, just as the neon bar signs downtown flickered and hummed to life, whispering Rusty, you won, you showed us who's boss, now use that self-control, show us how you can stop yourself after just one.

Rusty tried to sleep, but thought about Melanie instead, for hours, still awake when she was probably awakening. He pictured her in flannel, shining a flashlight, eyes dampened, closet after closet.

*

May 10th was the last day of Littmann's course, and the first day Rusty knew what he needed to do. He hadn't studied his lines. Fifteen minutes into the simulation, he had missed every cue.

Littmann, exasperated, called Interaction Node 63. "Okay, so ladies, Dave's childish little snit here: helpful or not? I'm sensing a big 'not.' In a true partnership, a Synergetic Symbiosis, to use my trademark-pending phrase, I would hope that The Dave would take his passive-aggressive hostility and channel it toward some honest, rewarding interplay with The Darlene, instead of gumming up the relationship gears with his sludge of negativity. But you need to make up your own minds. Ready devices."

The handhelds appeared in a white rash across the auditorium.

"Interact."

Keypads clattered like hailstones.

After ten seconds, the Results Monitor indicated 89% Not Helpful.

"Excuse me, but I'd like to call a Node too," said Rusty.

"You what?" said Littmann.

"I want to call a Node," repeated Rusty.

"You can't call a Node. We just had a Node. And besides, I call the Nodes. And one more thing, you've now received a Not-Helpful for the day, so you're in no position to be pushing the limits, Dave."

"But why can't I call one?"

"Because I am conducting the simulation, DAVE, that's why. An actor can't step out of the simulation, DAVE, that's also why, for to do so would inject inappropriate perspective into the situation. May I remind you, DAVE, that the key to my realistic Interactive Marriage Simulation methodology is, as I will rather eloquently state in my upcoming white paper, the limitation of actors' outside perspectives to only those that real people would experience at that moment. The perspective belongs only to them," gesturing toward the seats. "Years from now, when these students, whom I have the distinct privilege to instruct, find themselves in similar circumstances to the ones you both are rather painfully attempting to portray, they will remember (fondly, I think) their IMS experiences and be able to step back from their marital crises and assess their behavioral options with some degree of perspective."

"I thought you just said that realistic simulations cannot involve perspective," mumbled Rusty.

"Of course I did", shouted Littmann, banging the podium with his fist.

"So we need to keep perspective out of these realistic simulated problems so that some day they," pointing outward, "will be able to put perspective into realistic real problems?"

Littmann's face went momentarily blank.

"I'd like to request interaction on the possibility of Dave extending one Token of Endearment to Darlene right now," Rusty continued.

Littmann choked out his words. "No, absolutely not. No way. You're completely off script, Dave. You are supposed to be Emotionally Unavailable this week, remember? A Token of Endearment, this week? Are you kidding me? Do you enjoy being our human speed bump, Dave? Where was your Token of Endearment three months ago, during Infidelity, when your little supply room rendezvous with . . . what was her name . . ."

"Brandy," yelled out one of the sorority girls, the one named Brandy, who got to play Brandy.

"Right, when your little supply room rendezvous with Brandy over there just about doomed your simulated marriage to the simulated crapper? Huh, Dave? What's that? Did you say something? You can't expend a Token, Dave. I believe your emotional account is overdrawn."

Murmurs of approval rose from the dimmed rows of seats. The sorority girls were giving Littmann little mock fist-bumps.

"I'm serious," said Rusty. "I want an answer. Why can't Dave be there for Darlene right now?"

Melanie looked ill.

Littmann fumed. "Interaction Node 64," he stammered.

Rusty approached the podium, fists balling. "Now you wait just a damn minute . . ."

"Interaction Node 64!" Littmann cried out, louder, positioning the podium between himself and Rusty. "Consider the conundrum: our Dave, in a grievously misguided effort to focus your empathy on our Darlene, has succeeded instead in drawing your focus to his own antics instead of the CRS, the Core Relationship Stressor. It's a classic misdirection-objection. Okay then, Dave, what if I turn the tables on you a bit? You think what you're doing is right, and yet the scene isn't working—look at Melanie over there, she's absolutely sick. So, if something's wrong, and it's not you, it must be her. Ladies, your choice—do we replace our Dave with someone who is more, shall we say, minimally cooperative, or do we accept and attempt to work through the issue raised by our currently obstructivist Dave, and following his recommendation to replace Darlene in time for the final exam?"

"Hey, I never suggested replacing Melanie, I mean Darlene," said Rusty.

Littmann ignored him. "It's a simple choice. I would not be forthright with you ladies, however, if I didn't warn you that the effort involved in rehabilitating our current Dave would involve some degree of additional evening workshops and study groups, and we'd have to postpone the final. But that, of course, is your prerogative. Ready devices. Interact."

Rusty looked at Melanie. Melanie stared at her fuzzy slippers until the clicking subsided.

96% Replace Melanie.

Rusty was numb, but still breathing. He was at the bottom of a well, paralyzed, glued to a cot, surrounded by echoes of dripping water. It was the sound of a leaking life, its years draining away, its hopes dissolving. Without her acting gig, Melanie wouldn't be able to afford her mother's care, would never speak to him again, would start the gears turning that would lead straight to him spending the remainder of his years lofted and cotted and alone. A black hole yawned open beneath him, swirling and swallowing everything, but then there came a thin voice like a rope to grab onto, a man's voice, miles away, a far-off Littmannish voice thanking everyone for a rousing end to this semester's simulations. Distant applause spilled over the edge of the hole and rained down on him from above, from the auditorium full of women, and he clawed up the walls and followed it back to its source.

". . . and it's been my distinct pleasure to guide you young ladies through this semester's exploration of the complexities that muddle even the most rudimentary specimens of the male species, and the resulting impediments to healthy relationships that are bound to ensue. Dave, or shall

I say Rusty, (I guess I can go back to calling you that now!), I am duly impressed at the push-back during today's class. Quite stimulating, actually, for a final session. I wasn't sure you had it in you. You took it right down to the wire, but with that last-minute outburst of emotional maturity, you've nonetheless proven my hypothesis—that with weeks of helpful interaction on our part, the self-inflicted-wounding instincts of an inferior male can be altered to allow the formation of strong and lasting relationships. Ladies, excuse me, but before you leave, I'd be remiss if I didn't take a quick moment to thank my graduate assistant, Elizabeth Duffy, for pulling off the doubly-difficult assignment of portraying Melanie Grabowski portraying Darlene Dithers. Simulation within simulation! Well done, my dear. Do you ever wake up and forget your real name?"

Amid laughter and applause, students stood, gathered their things and filed up the aisles and out the rear doors of the auditorium. Elizabeth, acknowledging no one, disappeared into the locker room.

Rusty sat on the edge of the stage, nauseous and adrift. Littmann joined him. They were alone.

"Rusty, this isn't going to help right now, but I had my reasons. If I had told you that you were participating in a course called Inadequate Male Studies, you would have altered your natural instincts, right? Practiced up for the role? Artificially adjusted your actions, out of pride, to better fit some sort of macho stereotype? No, I couldn't have that. I'm a man of science, Rusty. I believe in the scientific method. This is going to be studied and published and then

52

picked apart by my naysayers, so I can't screw this thing up. This had to be a blind study, and the whole marriage simulation thing seemed like a reasonable placebo. You look stunned, Rusty. I'm sorry, I really am, but honestly, didn't you ever ask yourself why the class was comprised entirely of women? Didn't you check the course catalog? Didn't think to do that, right? I guess that's to be expected, that sweet naiveté. You'll come to understand, after the initial shock wears off, that my duplicity was necessary. I believe we'll even laugh about this some day. I'll see you and your riding mower out on the quad and I'll wave you down and you'll give me the finger and we'll just laugh. I'll say 'Hi Rusty' and you'll say 'Nope, the name's Dave' and we'll chuckle some more and I'll say 'How about signing up for another simulation?' and you'll say 'Simulate this, Littmann' and flip me off again. Ha ha!" coughed Littmann, stunted, as if doling out comfort in a Dixie cup, a grocery-store sample of some future camaraderie.

Rusty could only manage a word. Why.

Littmann put an arm over Rusty's shoulder. "Look, Rusty—imagine the entire male species as one big cherry pie. There are a lot of juicy bites in the center that everyone wants, or else wants to be, and then out on the periphery there's the crust, the part that most people leave on their plates when they've eaten all the good stuff. But we need the crust, don't you see, it's so necessary, because what's a pie without crust? A big sloppy mess of delicious fruit filling, that's what! We need guys like you, Rusty, because you give shape to the rest of us. You show us what we are by show-

53

ing us what we're not. But there's usually too much crust, isn't there, these big awkward hunks of dough, burnt on the edges, way more than what's needed to hold the thing together. So my career-defining brainstorm is this—what if I could take a bit of this crust and adopt it as a human renovation project, and get women to add their input throughout the process, and in the end transform some of that crust into more yummy pie-guts, which is what everyone really desires? This is the essence of my work—roaming the back alleys of masculinity and repatriating some of the most tattered and faltering fringe-dwellers of our species. I'm the anti-Darwin, Rusty, and you are my biggest success. I think you might even be ready to find a woman. You've spent your last day as crust, my friend. Let me be the first to welcome you to your new life." And with that, Littmann reached out his other arm and engulfed Rusty in a bear hug.

Rusty's arms hung limp at this side. He swallowed hard. Littmann released. Rusty felt his feet touch the floor, start to lurch toward the exit, but something made him stop and turn, something new, or newly-rediscovered, and the final and most indelible image Rusty took with him from all his years at Farmingham was the white flash of Littman's grin gone red from a collision with his fist.

*

Three hours later, Rusty slumped across the rear seat of a Greyhound bus. He had had forty dollars cash left in his pocket when he stumbled out of Ricky's Midtown Tavern, so he was headed somewhere that was exactly forty dollars away, the destination wasn't important, as long as rents were affordable and there were lawns that need mowing and it was miles and miles from Melanie, from Littmann, from Farmingham, miles from the backstage dressing room where the Ed the Janitor happened to be cleaning out the remaining contents of Rusty's locker. Ed delivered a grass-stained sweatshirt to the lost and found box in the front lobby of Townsend Hall, and the Rentals section of the Farmingham Sentinel to the trash. The only other item left in the locker, on the top shelf, was a cheap glass vase full of pink and white carnations. There was no note attached. Ed the Janitor shrugged. He decided he'd take the arrangement home and give it to his wife, who had just been saying the other day that she couldn't understand how she had ended up with exactly the kind of guy she never thought she would, the kind that would never bring a woman flowers just for the hell of it. I thought you got some kind of training, she had said. What the hell is your problem, Ed? Didn't that guy Littmann teach you anything?

*

"Brothers of the Salvageable Crust" originally appeared in *The Cincinnati Review*.

Ω

55

Columbus Road
by David Buchanan

At first, when the war was new and my marriage was perfect, it was special to come home. I would fly myself home from the war in my KC-10 refueling tanker, land in the afternoon at my base in the middle of New Jersey, go home, make love to my wife, and then go to my favorite crab leg joint for dinner. I would come down the stairs of the airplane; my wife would run across the tarmac and hold me and press her body to mine. I'd breathe in her clean shampoo and revel in her fresh smell and bright smile.

But coming home changed after that. We would embrace, and then I'd notice my own breath against hers. My coffee-and-Skoal-breath would overpower hers, and the moment I had been anticipating for months would pass. I never noticed the smell of jet fuel exhaust until I smelled her cool clean breath. I would introduce her to my crew, but after the first time, I began to feel embarrassed for her.

We were dirty, in day-old flight suits, unshaven and unfamiliar.

It got to the point that I just didn't want the other guys to even see her. Sharing—a tent, a cockpit, a shower—gets old during a deployment, and I wished she would stay away. "You are the only personal slice of me left," I told her. So she agreed to wait for me at home. For weeks thereafter, she would remind me that it was time to drop my locker-room talk; she'd sadly stare at her plate when I gnawed a steak bone in a restaurant. I convinced myself it was better this way. This time though, she wasn't waiting at the plane and she wasn't waiting at home.

There were eight of us back from this deployment. The commander made his hand-shaking rounds, and we got on a bus with the waiting family members. They were all awkward, the reunited families talking in hushed tones in the bus seats, checking familiar faces for any trace of the four-month separation. Babies cried and my flight engineer's four-year-old showed off a new scab from a fall at the playground. My nineteen-year-old boom operator joked about getting drunk that night in Philly. It was all forced, and I wanted to get away. We knew how to be with each other—had been doing it for hour after tedious hour for 124 days. But it hurts to be uncomfortable with the ones you love. As I got into my truck, my copilot shouted across the parking lot, "Deployments are easy. It's this going and coming shit that sucks."

I left base on a road that skirts New Jersey cornfields before hitting Interstate 295, the free highway to Philadelphia.

The green fields and mowed lawns were disorienting; so I left the window down and the radio up. They didn't expect me back to work for a week, and the lack of responsibility was sad and refreshing. The road ran through a small town called Columbus that I always enjoyed driving through. You entered town around a long sweeping curve that slowed down to 25 miles per hour, suddenly, just as you passed onto a main street lined on both sides with Philly-style row houses. The local police parked an old cruiser right behind the speed limit sign.

But there weren't any cops. Coming toward me in the opposite lane was a man in an electric wheelchair. He drove down the center of the lane with one hand gripping the chair's joystick. In the other, he held a two-liter bottle of Pepsi balanced in his palm, outstretched in front of his face. It was a trophy he wanted to share with the world, and for a moment I thought he was offering it to me. He had wild gray hair and wore no shirt. He was very tan under a thick mat of gray chest hair. He watched me watch him—we made eye contact—and I passed in a flash. I looked quick in the rearview mirror and saw him remove his right hand from the joystick. He raised it high above his own head, extended his middle finger, and flipped me off.

I didn't stop. Instead, I drove to an empty apartment in Philadelphia. Showered and cleaned, I turned on the television and saw that the general in charge of the war in Afghanistan was fired for saying the wrong things to the wrong reporter. I powered up my cell phone and listened to the one message left for me there. It was a week old. My wife's voice said she was tired of sharing. "People don't live this way," she said decidedly, "Marriage doesn't work this way."

I wish I could see the man on Columbus road again. I would ask him what he doubts in his own life. Does he regret? Do his decisions account for the loss? Where is he going?

Ω

Confetti

by Brett Garcia Rose

Seat 3C, Aisle

The night before my flight I lie to everyone, sitting in the back of a wine bar as Lauren hefts his tongue into my mouth, vaulting it slug-like over my teeth and arching it inside like a flashlight in a cave. He digs and explores and I pull back, leaning and fidgeting in my chair. It is a hypnotic, frustrating rhythm.

A grandfather clock swings on the wall behind him and pulls me along with it. The check lies flatly on the table. Gassy water sparkles in little pops. My phone buzzes and blinks. I wonder how much lipstick I have left. I wonder how much longer Lauren will sit here with his lukewarm tongue inside of me.

Soon enough our lives suck us out of the restaurant. Lauren kisses me goodbye and takes a cab uptown. I walk down. The air is cold and feels good on my bare legs. After a few blocks I get a text from Evan. *Almost done packing,* it reads. *Can you pick up some milk?*

I stop outside of our building and bend down next to an idling black Mercedes sedan with an older woman sitting in the passenger seat texting on a phone with a pink cover. I kneel down on one knee and stare at her through the tinted glass, reapplying my lipstick in shiny red arches. The woman doesn't look at me.

Later in bed I cannot sleep, tangling in the down comforter and cursing to myself as Evan murmurs in his dreams. At around two I get a text from Lauren. It reads, *you were amazing.*

The only way to deal with these types of people is to hate them and to go back to sleep.

But I don't. I stay awake deep into the morning, the words lying on my white silk pillow like dirt. As the sky lightens and I listen to Evan's steady breathing in the bed next to me I wonder how I got to this place, where the slide began. Some specific detour in a long line of miniature mistakes, some road I took and was too tired or too excited to turn back. I want to find that moment, and I want to correct it.

I loved Evan, once.

In court earlier today I smiled as the judge read his verdict. Everyone loses but me. Things are cut in half, and no matter what the size, half of something is less than everything, and what people refer to as *forever* is parsed out and scavenged by the courts, and by me, and by the greatest enemy of all; by time herself.

A divorce lawyer is never really married. We know how it ends so we save something for later, holding back some small part of ourselves where we think it will remain safe. We corral our new life into this model, idling down two roads, happy and distracted, not knowing what we know. But it never lasts. All of us, we seek pain. We hunger for it. We find it.

That small part we hold back is who we eventually become.

What I need from Lauren is his need for me. Sex, like eating or bathing, develops its own efficiency at the cost of intimacy. When I go to the supermarket, I don't browse. I already know what I want, where to get it and how much it will cost. In bed I become mean and efficient, my body taking over and dishing out the eloquence of my passion in sloppy, business-like efforts. Naked, I know what I want. I know where to get it. I know how much it will cost me. Lauren plugs a leak and keeps my marriage from crashing, but each time I get a little smaller. Each time I sink, a little deeper.

I still love you, Evan says yesterday, like the first day we met. He says it without looking at me, leaving the words on the table for me to collect later. But I don't. They sit there and they wait, baking into the wood, sifting into the dirt of lies and compromises until everything is covered in its bitter paste.

Sex is not love any more than methadone is heroin, but an end-stage happiness junkie will snatch it up in a second. It's not cheating. It's surviving.

Sometimes I think love is a tiny island in a great roaring river. You either hold on or you don't. You swim and you drift and love just dissolves. Once it lets go, you rush off, alone. You twist and spin and make inconsequential corrections, sometimes for years, until you land in the very same place you began from and convince yourself it's new.

I'll love Evan again someday. All that changes are the names.

The flight to Miami the following morning is a blur of first class martinis, of sarcasm and waiting and bickering and anger. Sera is difficult, I've barely slept, and Evan is polite and tentative in a way that infuriates me, and the guy across the aisle from me is a watcher. I can feel him staring at me. When I stand up to use the rest room, he struggles out of his narrow seat and follows me, creating pretend coincidences like men do. Everyone wants me. No one wants me. I hover and pee and when I stumble out of the little room he's right there, stopping me, telling me I'd be so much more beautiful if I smiled. He stands blocking the aisle, pleased with himself and his small bravery, handing over these words like a gift of feathers floating on his stale breath, and it's all I can do to not to punch him. He may as well call me mean and ugly. I smile and slide around him, duck-walking back to my seat in the turbulence, back to my husband and to Sera and to another form of turbulence.

Seat 3B, Center

Dear God. My class assignment for Monday is to write a letter thanking you and telling you what I think of the world you have created. I know you don't know me, I don't talk to you like some people do, but I'm here now and writing to you. My parents have been fighting a lot, mostly about the world, but I think it's really about each other. They watch the TV and say how bad everything is and how much worse it will all get and how there is no hope. They fight about money and work, about what my dad is gonna do and when he's gonna do it. It's like they stopped liking each other. I do that too sometimes, with my friends, and I don't know why. I think there's just something wrong with us that you need to fix, that you might have been too busy to notice. I think you've done a good job, mostly, but there are a few things I'd change if I were you. I'd make people be nicer to each other. I'd make people love each other and never fight, even when they don't agree. I'd like to see people sit down together on the couch and hug and try to understand each other instead of yelling, instead of slamming doors and breaking things and crying and running away. There's no reason to hate each other and to be so mad but we are, and it isn't right.

Also, I know you're gonna take my Nana soon, and that's ok I guess. She's tired and I don't think she wants to be here anymore. So I'll make you a deal. I'll let you have Nana if you do something for me, and since I never asked you for anything, ever, you should do it. I want you to make my parents love each other again. You can use them to see how it works, and it will work, you'll see, and the world will be a better place, and then you can do it to everyone else and the world will be an even *better* place.

I guess that's all I have to say for now. The plane is bouncing a lot and it smells funny, like someone's cooking something bad.

Seat 3A, Window

Cara's going to leave me after the funeral. I spend my time waiting, and remembering. Love does not die out like people say. The aging of love is a stripping away of its senses. The vision fails, and love cannot see. Then goes the touch; love cannot feel. Love loses its hearing and love hides and does not know what to do. It is a weakening, a fading back into the source. Love dissolves into hope, and hope is a dangerous, reckless thing, lying in wait like a predator, hiding in its cave for some new defenseless opportunity to drift into its arc.

In the end, love is dementia.

Cara used to live inside of me and take up my best space but I can no longer feel her. I can only see her from the outside, the silhouette of a familiar stranger. And I remember now all those small turns filled with choices unmade or made wrong, all those places where I could have turned it all around but didn't, believing always that there was more time, that she would wait until I finished some small inconsequential thing in a life filled with small inconsequential things.

We all want more.

We are a machine of flesh and hope now, of promises and routines and transparent barriers described into our days in a dead language we no longer care to decipher. We are a machine spinning out, drifting finally to a slow stop until the time comes when we just fall over, when we gather what's left and walk the rest of the way. And I can feel that time coming, that final moment, that last sad look, the clarity and sadness of things forgotten as we walk out in our separate shells, bewildered and waiting to be rescued.

Love is a race car that does not wait, piloted always by the incompetent, by the distracted, by the safe, by the forward-looking and the ever blind.

I lean over in my seat and press my head against Sera's curls until she looks up. She smiles at me, our foreheads touching, but I can see our sadness written on her face, and this gives me the strength to swallow my pain and my pride. As she turns back to her game I wonder what she'll learn, who she'll become. I see Cara in her, in her strength and temper and beauty, but also I see me. She is the best of both of us. What we hope to be and wish we were, and what we might have become in another, more perfect world. Through Sera we get to be more than we ever could have alone.

Cara has her first martini shortly after takeoff as she flirts with a guy across the aisle. The seatbelt light is on, the plane thrashing and bucking, but when she gets up to use the rest room he follows shortly after. I married a beautiful woman and I'm flattered when men make a run for her, but it's also disheartening, seeing strangers get the best of her now, the part that I had and lost, the part that will go on without me, to new places.

I watch her go as I always will.

Hours later as we cross the Atlantic the flight attendant informs us that we may need to divert to another airport. She doesn't say why, and the plane begins descending in jerky fragments, flung downward like a wet feather.

I look over at Cara, lost in her sad thoughts and more beautiful even than the day I first saw her, stranded at a turnstile with a faulty Metrocard, and I let her in, with me, in every way.

The Galley

I had a roommate in college who used to cut herself. We would see the faint scars on her arms and inner thighs and say nothing. Then one night we were walking home from a party and all very drunk, and someone asked why she cut herself. I swear I thought she would freak out and deny it, would get angry and indignant, but instead she just smiled and rubbed one of the scars. "People always assume that I am addicted to the pain, but they're wrong," she said, staring straight ahead and smiling, her eyes glossy in the reflected streetlights. "I'm not addicted to pain," she said. "I'm addicted to healing."

I sit strapped into my jump-seat in a pressurized aluminum tube knifing unnaturally through the skies, cheating time zones and racing ahead of life and all I can think is this: *we're all addicted to healing.*

Maybe that's why we hurt each other so much.

I told Jared about the baby last night and I feel worse for it, even less sure. When he asked who the father was there was a hurt slamming through me that I never could have imagined possible, a black weight crushing me. I cried for hours and screamed myself to sleep. This morning after securing the cabin and falling asleep against the galley counter, I asked myself the same question over and over.

Do I really want a baby as horrible as me?

Only the five of us hear the alarms. Steve sounds nervous as he announces the malfunction, which is pilot-speak for everything you don't want to say, for nothing anyone wants to hear. The words fling themselves out of the recessed speakers like wasps.

After the announcement there's a time lag before the fear sets in. People are at first angry, then bewildered, then helpful and comforting to one another, and finally they become cruel, mean and selfish.

We crash so we can live.

Steve says there's enough time, that it's a controlled descent, but he doesn't sound so confident. It's simple math, really, but that math sits atop unpredictable mechanics. Whatever happened down below, we don't really know. And what will happen in the next 20 minutes before landfall? We don't know that, either.

A fire on a plane slinging itself towards the ocean, well, there's nothing good about it.

Steve's words stream out of the speakers and spread through the cabin like confetti. We're not going to make land. Just before clicking off he pauses, and the passengers all stare at the cockpit door. No one breathes.

"The exits are clearly marked," he says.

All these people, sad and angry, bewildered, finally mean and cruel and selfish. In the end everyone wants to stand up, when it's too late. Everyone wants to be somewhere else, be *someone* else. Always, too late.

I decide to keep the baby. I decide to stop running. There are places in the world, I think, that don't hurt so much. Places where I can sit in the sand with the sun on my face and warm salty water sliding over my feet, next to someone I love. Anyplace but here, this fragile little tube, reaching and screaming over the whitecaps like a proud, dying thing, trying to leap over one last wave and reach land, any land.

The Cockpit

Control passes me off to the coastguard. I know what that means but there's nothing left to say. All I can do is pull into the wind at the last minute and try not to pitch. We can survive a water landing; it's been done before, even in the chop. But the swells worry me.

We watch them coming at us, graceful, angry things, pushing ahead their foamy white tips like claws. I try to measure the space between them and find a workable rhythm but it's chaos. I think of Lily behind me, strapped into her jump seat, scared. She rubs her belly. She tries not to cry.

The voices don't help so I turn off the alarms. Bill continues with the radio, keeping busy and distracted. The controls go softer. We float downward in roller-coaster humps.

Bill is 28 years old, and scared. I'm older, and more scared.

At fifty feet, I feel closer to heaven than I ever imagined I could. Bill instructs the passengers to assume the crash position. We're going in. I see the crests in the full moon, the angry foam tips grasping upwards for us. The spray coats the windshield, and then there's nothing left to see.

We go in gently at first, skimming over the first few swells and dropping speed, but then we pitch hard, tail over. The windshield holds. I think of Lily. I think of the baby. And I see my life.

Miami-Metro Hospital, Room 201, Intensive Care

The nurses dressed me this morning. It's the first time I've been in anything other than a gown in months, and it feels better than I thought it might have. Cara and Sera should be here soon, with Evan. Last night was the worst yet and I worried that I might miss them, but morning came, and I'm still here.

I don't have much time left and I do want to see all of them, to say goodbye properly. It's a strange thing, getting old, peaceful in a way I never expected. What happens is this, and it's hard to explain but I'll try. What happens is you separate from your body. You watch it tire and fail, and it's a little sad and a little frustrating, sometimes even angering. It's like when we broke down in the car on the way to Pennsylvania so many years ago, Frank and Cara and I, broke down and just sat in the broken car, sticking in the plastic seats and watching the heat curl off of the blacktop as we waited for someone to come along and help us. It's just a different kind of time, the waiting.

It's sad to see Evan and Cara, to see the arrogance of their youth, the way they waste time like it is in endless supply, like they can just go to the store and pick up some more when they run out. But you can't do that. You can't. Trust me on that. When you run out of time, you can't fix anything. All you can do is to wait, wait for that next thing to come along while you sit in your broken body, wait for whatever it is that comes and moves you out of the way while everyone else races by.

The nurses huddle outside my room in a small cluster watching television, some new tragedy got hold of their attention. It's always the same thing, the news, and they don't show me anything I'd care to see. We live in a beautiful world, every second is another wonder, but all they show is the worst bits. And now, at the end, not knowing where I'm going, not knowing what else there may be, no, they can't help me. No one can.

I lie in bed listening to the nurses whispering and conferring, and all I can do is to wait. I look at the door, and think; *it's nearly time.* One of the nurses, the young one with the pretty black hair, talks into a phone and looks at me with a sad smile and hooded eyes. No one feels good in a place like this. No one wants to die.

I smile at her and my eyes wander upwards, watching the red exit sign above the door. The nurse looks away. Death hovers at the end of my vision like an old lover standing behind airport glass. All of us, racing through life. All of us, waiting.

I watch the sign. I smile. And I wait.

Ω

Dream of Crows
by Malcolm Campbell

During the coroner's inquest into the matter of your death, a well-meaning friend or relative will step forward with your affidavit stating that you read *Dream of Crows* because you saw it in your spouse's copy of *Corvus,* heard several clerks at Barnes and Noble speculating about its deeper meanings, or—more likely—because you were intrigued by the probable connection between the short story and an odd string of assisted suicides in a Florida swamp. But, were you alive to testify, you would tell it true, as you well might if you survive truths no man should know. You sense these truths already; you feel you're reading these words now because you were called to read them now and, by the same token, that when the time comes you will follow their siren song out the north road to the old cemetery where a crow sits next to the open grave.

Ask yourself one question: "What do I remember?"

Do you remember telling a friend—or was she really the friend you thought she was?—that "I'm finally to the point in my life where I have nothing left to lose by tempting fate?"

No, of course not, for if you did, you wouldn't be risking more than you know at this moment. But, think back in time. It might help.

*

Six Months Earlier

"Someday an oracle will tell you this: 'But, think back in time. It might help.'" She tells you, and you sigh aversively to remind her that this is exactly the kind of circular conversation you deplore on a first date when—quite frankly—you're seeking less wordy pleasures.

"Will it help?"

"Thinking back in time? Sure, if you think back within three months," she says.

"What if I don't?"

She laughs and this bothers you because her eyes are dancing and light as though she knows something sluggish and heavy about you and is simply letting it slip away into the darkness where alligators and ghosts out in the swamp will consume it like so much road kill.

You watch her eat her steak in the flickering light of the candles. She eats like a savage. Perhaps she will consume you later in the evening.

"Nice gazebo," you say when she looks up and licks the A-1 Sauce off her lips.

"Eddie-Ray built it."

"Who?"

"My husband."

"Husband?"

She shrugs and pours herself another margarita. She tops off your glass, too. You're going to need it.

"Most people my age are married by the time they get to my age."

You glance back at the sepia-colored cinder block house flanked by weeds and slash pine trees. The windows are dark except for the small, isolated glow of a cigarette behind the sliding glass doors in the center of the house.

"That's him, isn't it?"

"He likes to watch."

"Watch what."

"Me."

"What about me?"

"You're of no consequence unless you touch me."

"What if I do?"

"You know how to find out."

You finish your drink while concentrating on the cigarette. It glows brighter when he takes a drag but not bright enough for you to see anything other than a rather large pair of binoculars focused, presumably, on her.

"I'm finally to the point in my life where I have nothing left to lose by tempting fate," you announce.

"I jimmied up his wheel chair," she says.

"Good."

She blows out the candles.

As you read, don't you remember?

How ghostly pale she is in the cloud-filtered moonlight when she steps naked out from under her little black dress.

How she runs down a narrow path behind the gazebo part the tangled titi thickets into the swamp.

How the cigarette continues to glow with no apparent malice behind the sliding glass doors.

How deathly quiet it is.

How you shed your clothes and follow her through the swamp to a cemetery on reclaimed high ground encircled by fetterbush, more titi and sweetbay magnolias, and how she stands, holding a single candle in front of her breasts, next to a weeping stone angel.

How she whispers, "Fate loves a man who risks all for a brief chance to play with fire."

How the night screams and is consumed.

*

Three and a Half Months After That

In your estimation, you're a practical man, but after three and a half months of inexplicable sexual abstinence you wonder what hideous karma has found its way into your utilitarian bedroom. Your wife, to say the least, is curious.

You complain of nightmares and she believes you because she hears you talking in your sleep.

"You said, 'just one more open grave,'" she says.

"How odd."

"You need to get help and I'm not saying this just because I've been so lonely," she says while she butters her breakfast toast and you stare past her red hair and her sheer nightgown and watch the trash man sling the blue recycling bin into the yard next to the morning paper.

"I'm sorry," you tell her. You're not sorry but you want to be. "How long has it been?"

"You haven't touched me since the night before your last business trip."

"What business trip?"

"Your three-and-a-half-months-ago business trip to north Florida," she says with an evolving distant look in her green eyes. "What happened there? Did the sun burn you to a crisp on a sugar-white beach? Did a shark eat your manhood in St. Andrews Bay? Did you run out of gas on highway 98 while fleeing from something bigger than both of us in Panama City?"

"Panama City," you manage to say, in spite of the scattered puzzle of memories that are dancing upon your mind as though *touched me* is a post-hypnotic suggestion.

"Oh, I remember," she is saying. "You drove down to consult with the hotel owner with a deal that went sour. Mike what's his face who was drunk when he called for help after slamming down one whiskey sour too many. Did you get drunk in Panama City and wake up in some woman's bed with a sour feeling in your heart?"

"Really sour." You respond more or less on automatic pilot because the words *touched me* are not your wife's words, not until she just said "You haven't touched me since the night before your last business trip."

They're words out of an old movie, something on cable, something you must have watched after the hotel owner with the sour deal called it a night. The movie, a black and white tale about crows, an axe murderer in a wheel chair and your recent dreams are tangled inside your head. Tangled like a titi thicket.

You look across the table. She's finished her toast, had time to clear away her plate and coffee cup and leave the room in her see-through red lingerie that you had no impact on you whatsoever. She's right, though; you haven't wanted her since you came home from the trip. You can't imagine wanting her, touching her, as she puts it.

According to the paperwork in your briefcase, you found a way to save Mike's company. "Yay, whiskey sours for everybody," you shout at the empty chair on the distant side of the kitchen table. You found Mike's salvation, but lost yourself due to sugar-white beaches, sharks or running out of gas on highway 98.

You're out of gas now, that's for sure.

As your wife leaves for work you say, "I'm going back to bed."

"Good," she says and backs out the door into the bright morning.

You leave a blank sheet of paper on the nightstand on the off chance you'll dream about something and have the presence of mind to write it down. When you wake up, you discover a page containing over 500 words of dream memories in perfectly penned Italics:

Bluesy hotel bar. Old guitar player from New Orleans. Hotel owner Mike saying drinks are on the house. Bottom shelf whiskey. His assistant, Angelique, dark, sultry, barely in a black dress, telling you on the house occurs once in a blue moon. She is standing closer than Mike.

I've never seen a blue moon, I tell her.

I'll show you after I prepare myself.

All the talk settles down to safe acronyms like P&L and ROI while the singer performs "Them Ol' Conjure Woman Blues." He's playing that for you, Mike says before he passes out.

Me?

The bartender says Angelique's a conjure woman; she talks with crows.

Why, I'm wondering out loud.

Suddenly returned from preparing herself, Angelique says crows are the guardians of knowledge.

The wind is strong and salty along the coast road while I doze in the shotgun seat of her old MG. She's singing, one arm around me, one on the wheel. Then we're naked, dancing around the edge of a cemetery, your blue moon baby she says, and I say it doesn't look blue.

Ever made love in an open grave? she asks. Before I fashion an answer she's humming bluesy songs in a key so minor they could cry a man's heart out.

These are strange epitaphs, I tell her as she jumps down into a cozy, freshly dug hole. "He touched me," that's what they all say, I say, and she says everyone's gonna touch somebody sometime and so will you if you don't undo the spell.

Spell as in spelling bee?

Can you spell voodoo? Make love to your wife three times in three months and the spell goes away.

If not what, if not what, if not what?

Want me now? she asks, I'm here, close and hot in this cold hole, do you?

If not what?

Oh, she laughs and puts her hands on me. If not, then you'll never see me again and the sweet world take you. Have me now because Eddie-Ray forgives the first time out upon this altar of the blue moon where crows dream about us coming together. Now, have me now and I'll have you forever unless you cheat on me with your wife.

What about the second time out, I ask, thinking it a fair query, to which she replies I send men to heaven for an hour before Eddie-Ray sends them to hell for an eternity.

Oh my, I say.

But they don't mind, she says, and besides that, they can't help themselves.

Oh my, I say again.

I see in your eyes you're helpless already.

The guitar man is playing older songs when I return, the place thick with cigarette smoke and the smell of musk and I see the bartender watching me through a bottle of cheap whiskey. You're grinning like a hyena, he informs me.

Why?

If not what? he asks, and I say I'm a normal person with a normal smile.

You've gone past normal, to the swamp and back, beyond the grave and back. You did the conjure woman, didn't you?

I most surely did.

I thought so; you're a marked man, a man looking for an axe in the side of his head.

Pour me something; pour me a tall cold one.

*

It's time.

As you pack your suitcase, you wonder what you'll do if she comes back inside and tells you she's skipping work so you can make love all day, when all you know a dream calls, has been calling, because a woman down on the coast said crows dream the world into place and we're stuck in those dreams unless we wake up and open our eyes. You cannot control your eyes.

You're talking to your suitcase because your wife is getting farther away, passing the bank, heading into her day.

"I'm heading into my day, too, and my day is a trip to a holy place because truth appears suddenly to lovers and blind men. I'm no lover, not lately. You see, I asked her what would happen if we didn't make love in that open grave beneath the blue moon that didn't look blue."

You finish your bloody Mary while you think about Angelique's body next to you, on top of you and underneath you while you died over and over and went to hell over and over and if that wasn't holy you didn't know what was.

And she answered you like this: "If you don't make love to me now, you are but a crow's nightmare."

God help you, but you didn't want that.

You wonder if an axe stuck in the side of a guy's head hurts more or less than a meaningless life. It's something to ponder on the trip to Florida, en route to that paradise of sweetbay magnolias, tangled titi and blue moons.

Out of habit, you lock the front door.

*

As you approach the final words of *Dream of Crows* and sense a change in the weather, you wonder if you should leave a note, a goodbye of sorts here in the magazine or on the kitchen table, a "thank you" for time served, but all the crows in the front yard have to say about that is this: "Truth appears suddenly to lovers and blind men."

Ω

Entropy
by Dino Parenti

Twenty-nine years behind me, and it all boils down to a single wretched dilemma: can't light the cigarette my hands can't even hold.

Just getting to it meant nudging it up from my shirt's pocket with a shaky, swollen knuckle in order to fish it out with my teeth, and even then only the bottom row grazed filter; nothing left between the top incisors but jagged, fractured roots.

Running my tongue along them, and a dormant feeling is rekindled. Six years back and three weeks into my first stint in prison, and the very same broken-glass sensation had lingered long after the crowns had been put in. Phantoms, they're called. Nerves screaming accounts of renounced body parts in pitch-black rooms.

Read about that in an AMA journal. Nothing much to do on the inside but count time and read your fill. That first stretch, conjured out of some overblown vehicular misunderstanding involving the police while the boy was still fresh in his mother's belly, busied myself dissecting the dictionary front-to-back between soaking up my weight in prose. Misters Raymond Chandler and Isaac Azimov were eagerly devoured between bench-presses, brawls, and the occasional smuggled four-twenty.

By my last stint, could parse Hamlet and Macbeth to give the average Oxford don a run for his money. Words and I were a natural fit. Better than man and I.

Every time I'd wonder how better or worse a sort I'd be today had I known this during my gentler years, the final verdict always seems to suggest that it wouldn't have mattered one damn bit.

As for the reasons I wound up penned on those subsequent occasions, there were only bureaucratic ones. Nothing *moral*. Wasn't a person who got thrashed that didn't deserve it in the biblical sense. Missed the boy's birth as a consequence though, and all but the first two years of his life. Jenna would bring him for visits, and she'd send the occasional picture, but I don't know him. Not how a father should. Only been around in the flesh for four of his ten years. The other six, subsisted on daydreams and the scribblings of dead men, gazing out a tiny meshed porthole at the slow fan of constellations, always wary of returning to the world to play more ill-fitting roles.

Five teeth were vacated from my mouth that first time—over a curl bar disagreement, far as I can recall—and had I occasion to do it over again, would've opted to leave them broken at the gum line as reminders to pick and choose my battles more wisely.

My sitting on this curbside doesn't quite qualify as an example of such indiscretion, dribbling blood and memories into a coursing gutter, the bar's sign winking nasty in the corner of my eye. But neither are there intentions on fixing these teeth.

Lee's, it says in simple block letters. As much a declaration of status as proprietorship. A cut-rate yellow marker festooned with stars. Stars shooting from the curves in the letters, forming a pattern surrounding the name. Even the apostrophe's a star, the biggest one of the lot. Jenna told me once the scientific term for the patterns stars make in the night sky, but damn if it's not fusing at the moment. For what it's worth, recall her whispering to me one time after lovin'—in all likelihood, the very session that yielded the boy—that space is an endless, expanding womb where galaxies and stars, planets and comets, gametes and lust smash into each other to create or extinguish life.

To which can now be added: hands colliding into faces to alter courses.

But all this pondering is so much rigmarole now. Jenna's not taking me back. Not after this. No one stays after this. Not with the boy to consider.

*

Met Jenna in the middle of a balmy August meadow while she was part of a college astronomy club on a field-trip to watch the Perseid meteor showers.

Wasn't there for the meteors myself. Was too bottom-heavy with blood and booze, my eyes disinclined to climb beyond whatever fetching chest they found purchase on.

She stood on a tiny mound of crabgrass, hair exploding in blood-orange highlights, eyes poring over the sky as if it were the Dear-John letter from some philandering god. Drawn in by this solemn air, as much for how she filled out a pair of black tights, I was ill-prepared for how tough a score she would prove to be.

Any more room on that bump? had been my come-on after sidling over. Like I'd said, bottom-heavy.

She about-faced fully to take in the interloper, gnawing thoughtfully on the end of a pen, offering little but the driest of appraisals before resuming her previous peacocked posture, leaving me to wonder about the hints of ink peeking up from the base of her shoulder blades.

Had no counter for her audacity, nor for her sudden shifts in attitude, as when I started to walk away, convinced that I'd struck out, only to have her hop down to snag my hand in order to jot down her name and number on it. Delved into her deep blues whilst she did this, engrossed by the eclipse that pulled gradually across her face, regrets and apprehensions skittering underneath and pooling black over the cobalt.

Call me within twenty-four hours, or forget about me, she said before turning on a heel to retake her mound.

Should've forgotten about her right there and then probably, but it was never my way to leave something unexplored on account of rough terrain.

*

Damn near waited till the eleventh hour to call her the next night.

What's your biggest dream? she asked. Even if it may never come true?

Her first question after the awkward pleasantries. Going right for the throat. That disarmed me even further, but I gotta admit, I liked it. Spared me the horrors of ice-breaking at least.

You'll laugh, I told her.

I'm not an easy laugh. But feel free to try.

Alright. Guess at some point I was wanting to be a chef.

Took her a while to respond, a finger tapping a Johnny Cash tempo on the side of the phone the entire time.

I don't see anything funny there. That's sweet actually.

You'd be in the minority then. Okay, your turn.

I'm scared to tell you.

Why? 'Cause you're worried I'll laugh?

'Cause I worry you won't.

Try me.

The slow-drawn cello of her breathing put the whammy on me. Truth be told, I could've listened to it all night, but she only offered a minute of this refrain.

If you ask me out, I'll tell you about it on our first date.

She then prefaced any further discussion by saying straight out that she was the daughter of Lee Allister Malone. Lee ran the biker bar out on Highway 64. Vietnam vet and all-around top alpha dog, he was the town's official, off-the-record trustee. Even the cops would retain his services now and again when discretion and a little extra muscle was required.

Jenna left all that out, of course, but there wasn't a soul in town who wasn't already privy to that.

*

At the edge of a velvet-black pond that went by about eight different names—a spot where, in the spring of '89, Trisha Eccleston was saintly enough to welcome me into manhood—I set up a picnic for our first date.

What draws you to damaged goods? she asked rather pointblank as I spread the blanket over the sodden earth. Are you striving for some Christian ideal, or are you just a garden-variety masochist like most others?

Wasn't sure how to reply, so I reddened and shrugged before claiming my corner of the quilt. To my surprise she sat down beside me instead of opposite, and that was fine. Took her a while to squeeze my hand back, though it was she who'd taken mine first. We spoke little while gobbling mini-mart hotdogs and pink snowballs amongst a pollen-drift of fireflies. Occasionally we'd titter over the sandpipers jousting against the pink down of the horizon, but mostly we just ate.

At one point, noticed several stray pink coconut flecks on the corner of her mouth, though when I reached up to dab them off with a napkin, she shoved my hand away. Umbrage revved instantly under my skin, but it was faraway, uncertain, refracted, and as my mouth opened-and-closed in aborted attempts to say something, she grabbed my hand again to squeeze sweetness and amends.

I wipe my own dribbles and spills, she said.

A heron screeched its forlorn *roo-roo* into the night, and this seemed to umpire us back into the sweet stasis of just before.

After a while my eyes crept over to the peculiar ink on her left shoulder blade I'd first caught sight of when we met, and which I'd noticed again earlier whenever she'd turn to the basket. A botched job; someone had tried to fill out a flower from something of a misshapen star. When she caught me peeking at it, she stiffened, but her eyes remained hooked to mine, and I could tell it took every ounce of courage to keep them from fleeing her skull.

Blunder from my youth, she said at last through a bashful smile. Got the starfish 'cause I admire its ability to self-replicate. I used to think myself resilient like that. That I could handle my own, you know? But as I got to understanding the order of things, I found I better related to flowers. It's okay to die, if it means returning again stronger in the spring. Sometimes as a different species if need be.

My confusion must've flared white-hot, for she smiled more assuredly and dabbed a finger on my nose. Would hit me later that anyone that's ever touched me before in a similar fashion usually got swatted at the least.

I wanted to be an astronomer. My mama bought me a telescope when I was eight and set it up in our attic window. My father . . . he wasn't too keen on me wasting my time daydreaming about outer space. Ragged me about it every chance he could, pissing off my mama something awful every time. Then one day, not too long after mama had passed . . . I suppose to make up for things . . . he painted the attic black before adding green and blue phosphorescent stars. Only they looked more like starfish than anything up in the sky.

Her mouth pressed into a hard straight line that tautened all her features.

That's neat, I said, compelled to say something lest her entire face collapse into her throat. You can still follow through though, you know. You ain't but what, twenty-three? And you're obviously into heavenly bodies, so . . .

I'm twenty-seven, and no. No, it's fine as the occasional outdoor hobby, but it's . . . too much focus in confined, solitary spaces for this girl. I am staying in the sciences though. Studying nursing at the college. Trying to anyway.

She shivered hard and sudden. Couldn't say if it was just the cooling air that did it, but I shimmied over against her anyway and she eventually listed her head against my shoulder and quietly sighed. Huddled in this sweet melancholy, her red tendrils snaking down my chest and back, I tried to drape my arm around her, but she shrugged it off.

I wanna tremble against you, she said, and this time she took both my hands into hers, cupping them as if to keep warm a kitten. I've always had . . . a more natural disposition for pacifying ogres and demons anyway. Some might call it a compulsion, like chewing your nails. But for me it's . . . like an obligation. Built up a few too many cul-de-sacs in the brain as a result though, and I can't help wondering if self-interning might help reconnect some of those roads.

She laughed this off after a pause, and I followed suit because it was uncouth to leave her hanging during such a lonesome outpouring, and it was something we'd continue to do every date thereafter whenever she'd bring up the casual threat. But when she actually, finally did it, the reality was still a roundhouse to my throat. This was Jenna's power. Her unique and unnerving inexorability.

*

These hands scold me more by the minute. Feel as if they're being backed over by a steam roller while on fire. If not for the fact that the gutter's runoff stems from the carwash down the street, I'd dip them into the running sluice. Some of the gashes in my knuckles run deep however; the nicotine wash of bone even peeks through in a few places from under the ticking of fat and muscle, and I don't mind saying that it's a sobering thing to see your naked inner workings so blatantly.

There's also an upturned mole cricket lying on the frothy shoals of the discharge where I'd considered placing my hands. It's a big sucker, at least three inches long, and ugly in ways that almost cycle back to beauty. It kicks at the air with its hind legs, but every turn it achieves towards dry asphalt is instantly undone by the current as it catches on the back of its spade-shaped head.

For a while this grotesque little metronome fascinates me, and as I consider whether to turn it over with the tip of my boot, or pulverize it with the sole of said footwear, I'm just as befuddled by what that damn star pattern is called, bounced up from Lee's sign by the swirling black water.

Wasn't till I was out and struggling with the baby-steps of deferred fatherhood that Jenna confessed that the boy may not even be mine to begin with.

The day of his third birthday party, as I helped him fix a church out of Legos he'd accidentally elbowed the steeple off of, she kept corner-eyeing me and the boy. It was the contained agitation of someone braving a water moccasin swimming figure-eights between her calves. Wasn't till the boy was clapping and shouting *tower, tower!* at our finished masterpiece that I realized I was echoing the same look her way. Didn't even see it when the boy karate-chopped the top off the steeple again; heard him wind up and *hee-ya!*, and when the spire tumbled by my feet, it was only the tin cans of our eyes whirring static across a concave of twine that kept me from reaching back to grab him by the arm, shirt, throat, whatever my hands could wrap a fist around.

Later that night as we cleared up streamers and paper-plates smeared with green GI-Joe frosting, she paused mid-sweep to stare out the window for a while at wayfaring dandelion spores that the moon lit up like pearls.

I had a lapse a couple of months before you went away, she said, nibbling the inside of her bottom lip bloody. But I didn't say anything 'cause he has your ears and your strut. I just loath the thought of . . . pretense between people trying to care for one another.

Can't say I was surprised by her overstep. We were never fully invested in cohabitation terms. Still, I simmered over the possibility that not an hour earlier I'd helped some other man's issue blow out his candles. I'd only been out a month.

When I brought up the idea of a DNA test that night in bed, she rejected it outright. Saw no point to it, and it shocked me how easily I'd yielded to her. Suppose most men feel deserved of wealth and power, but rarely of love, and I was still in the midst of reconciling this. But she had the grit to take on both my bullheadedness and endless rumination. That, and a seer's prescience to wait out my imminent caving.

Ultimately we agreed to continue raising the boy as if he was fully ours, but in the places where my deeper, more ancestral goliaths lurked, this would always trouble me.

*

Didn't meet Lee for years, and when I did, it was purely by happenstance.

The boy was four, and we were at the store that day for toiletries and such. Had just come out a few weeks prior after a six-month bit for smashing the storefront of the local union delegate who was on the take and screwing us on overtime wages. Prick would off himself a month later, and from all accounts, the funeral had been a rollicking affair.

Was picking out a toothbrush and stealing awed glances at the boy's evolving features when I heard his name called. The voice pulled us both to the end of the aisle where Lee stood, a roll of paper towels jammed under a primate's arm. The rest of him was just as chiseled and impressively solid, culminating in a series of cauterized welts that spilled down his bald head like dried riverbeds.

The boy considered his grandfather through guarded eyes, making no move to advance, and for a while this is how they stood, mirroring the other's cant, Lee smiling a mash of pride and inquiry before finally advancing towards us. When he got to where he was parallel with the boy, he paused to run a quick hand atop his head.

Hello, Dale, he said. Be sure to tell your mama I hope she's well.

He kept dripping his hammerhead's smile, and I was glad the boy just stared mutely back, even as Lee pulled something from his shirt pocket and placed it into the boy's hand: an orange starfish about the size of a half-dollar.

When Lee leveled his pallid, grey eyes at me, I glimpsed for just an instant the ruin of Jenna's course, preserved for some cagy posterity within the cosmic swirl of his pupils where the war still raged for him, likely for all time.

What he said next was muttered through a smirk, and only its obscurity in the moment kept my fists wedded to my thighs. He recognized my restraint though, the confirmation made evident in his languid head-to-toe sizing up of me before sauntering off to the register.

Ah, the surrogate . . .

*

Jenna's final meal before leaving for the institution was a soufflé.

Normally I'd make them for her every Thursday because Fridays she didn't work and she could sleep in and not worry about feeling bloated while on her feet for ten hours a shift at the hospice helping dying people forget the inevitable for at least a few moments a day. But this had been a Monday, and the particulars of the day had done their part to soil her mood.

One of the old-timer's tortoises had died. Because the man had no family, all of his love poured into his terrarium. Too broken to even peer into the tank, Jenna assumed the task of burying it for him. Because that's what she did. It's what she'd done it for all the boy's hamsters and goldfish. Even done it for all the flowers in the house.

When I'd suggested keeping the shell as a paper-weight because it evoked the prehistoric, her eyes flickered solar-bright.

Nothing expired is to be hoarded, she said. The dead gets buried and stays that way.

Never came close to fearing a man the way I feared Jenna in that moment, as much for what she might do to me as to herself should the edict get violated. But I digress.

Jenna enjoyed watching me make soufflés. The boy would usually be asleep by then, so it would just be the two of us in the kitchen. The sight of me undertaking something delicate that also carried a high failure rate was the only thing beside the boy that put the sun in the woman's eyes.

Those moments, it was easy to forget that anything called aphasia or Hypomania flourished behind that sapphire scrim.

The greenhorn baker in her found my striving for betterment inspiring, and this jump-started her into baking cookies. She even bought a cookie-cutter set of astronomical shapes, and on weekends would make a dozen moons, comets, rockets, and UFOs for me and the boy to enjoy throughout the week. Odd that there was never a star in the bunch, but I assumed someone had pinched the pattern from the box in the store.

The one time she tried to tackle a soufflé, she mangled it. Came home that day and found her pouting in the kitchen, the cloven skulls of about a dozen cracked eggshells strewn about the counter.

How the hell do you make these without going mad? she asked.

Guess it's like building model airplanes, or chopping firewood, or lovin', I said. If the directions are halfway decent, the rest is intuitive.

Then I'll just watch you be intuitive from now on, she huffed before storming off for a shower.

Fine by me, I thought. Didn't mind one bit engaging in what pretty much amounted in my book to a paint-by-numbers affair, so long as she kept gazing at me with those sober blues as if I were father, son and husband all rolled into the same body.

The Monday before they came to take her away, I cracked an egg to start a new soufflé, but nothing spilled out. When I split the shell further it revealed a partly developed embryo. It had a way to go yet, but already there were tiny, budding feet, feathers, and a beak. The nascent slit of an eye.

Jenna was stuck at work, but the boy had been up late and was perched up at the island counter watching me cook. For a while he stared at the tiny fetus cupped in my hand, and gradually, as though his bones intoned something his brain couldn't give melody to, he began transferring concerned inquiry from his glacial blue eyes into my dark brown ones. His regard unnerved me so fully that I couldn't even remember stuffing the chick down the drain and flipping on the disposal. The jet-plane roar of it sure augured at my ears though; could even feel the crunch in my teeth, and without warning my gorge began scuttling up my throat before I managed to beat it back down.

Was it ever going to grow up? the boy asked. Not with the jump in pitch at the end like with the inquiries of most children, but staid all throughout. The way a scientist would ask it.

Took me a moment before I could gather myself enough to tell him, With enough warmth and time, who could say?

By the time Jenna came home, the blades were cutting nothing but air. When she asked what it had been, I replied that the water wouldn't drain. She eyed me long then as if trying to verify whether or not I were indeed the ghost from a forgotten past she just recognized before reaching up to dab at the flowering scar above her left eye.

In averting my gaze from her mark, it fell upon the boy's who promptly offered a single abdicating nod, tiny fingers braided at his navel.

When the turtle's shell turned up a week later as we tilled the soil in the flower beds, he extended the same silent reassurance at me, but she was already gone by then.

Nudge the mole cricket with the tip of my boot, and it kicks like mad to latch one of its hind legs to my foot while the knee joint of the other anchors itself within the lip created where the swale meets the asphalt. All the while the flotsam wakes across the Triceratops-like plating of its neck, threatening to draw it in.

My hands feel as though a new pair is trying birth out of them, and all I can wonder is what Jenna could do to soothe them, though why she would even try after this night . . .

Another cold green filament of meteorite scribes the ink above before disappearing. The transient autographs of specters. They've been zipping by at a good clip for the last ten minutes, about one every thirty-seconds, and from all around me in some Dolby level of castigation, human voices *ooh* and *ah* through the trees at the spectacle.

A coughing fit seizes me, and from deep in the well of my throat rumbles up the detritus from my earlier engagement. Lean myself over the cricket to hack out the thick dollop of frothy, bloody saliva, but it misses wide, catching the corner edge of the curb where it eventually slithers into the soapy cataract.

Between the archipelagos of suds, the stars from Lee's sign struggle to twinkle through, but I glance away beforehand and peer up at the sky. Don't need to look at it to know their pattern is trying to mimic the same shape as the constellation Leo. Stars hundreds of light years away that when strung together by crude human hands take the shape of a warped coat hanger. Yet they're nowhere close to each other. Jenna obsessed on those expanses, and would often whisper about them in bed to me when I couldn't sleep.

Many of those stars are gone now. All those boiling cauldrons of elements, and all that's left of them is their light. Their ancient death rattle. Distance can falsely impart proximity. From far enough out, Sequoias standing a football field apart could appear to belong to the same grove of saplings . . .

Asterism. The patterns that stars make as we see them from the Earth. It comes to me at long last, just as a lone police siren crowns through the night's balmy exhale from no particular direction.

*

Took the boy to watch the meteors fall. The Leonids. Jenna was coming home in a week, and she asked over the phone if I would take him so he wouldn't miss it.

It was unseasonably hot for November, and the cicada droned their score for the world until it enveloped me so thoroughly that after a while I stopped noticing them. A few dozen people had gathered at the upper holler by Highway 64, some sitting on blankets, some getting their bake on in the beds of trucks. Even ran into my cousin and her new husband, this runty lapsed Pentecostal-preacher with an atoll of healed snake-bites spiraling up his right forearm. He came off decently enough, though his chronically pursed lips reeked of so much self-righteousness being kissed into the ether, and it got me thinking the whole time we talked as to why men spent centuries conjuring gods, only to then turn around and attempt the roles themselves.

The boy and I staked out a spot in the middle of a wooden bridge near the same area where I'd met his mother eight years and four stints earlier. Across the way, opposite the highway, rippled the piss-amber lights of Lee's bar, and it took the boy asking me why my nostrils kept flaring before I could calm down.

The celestial show soon commenced with a pair of yellow-green filaments stippling overhead from the north, skipping across the atmosphere like the brightest scaled coins. Our legs stirred the air over the dark pond water, and as though pardoned from gravity for a moment, we would often look down to watch the falling refuse of a shedding comet getting slurped up, the illusion dampened now and again by guppies dimpling the surface for mosquitos.

Better than through some attic telescope, huh? I said to the boy.

Had my arm draped around his shoulders, and when he shrugged to my comment the shudder of his nerves was the physical embodiment of the wistful looks his mother would sometimes cast helter-skelter into the horizon.

Mama wouldn't let me up there, he said, his voice a reedy, matter-of-fact trill. I could see the telescope from the street. Big and white. Up high in the attic window when we would visit. But mama said I wasn't ever to go up there. Especially with grandpa. She said it was a dangerous place. The floors were soft, and we could fall through.

Meteorites soon began tearing up the sky like tracer fire. With every streak the crowd whooped and cheered ever louder, yet I felt myself plunging into a morass that was soon spinning as a singularity in the pit of my stomach. The harder I pondered the disintegration above us, the less I could shed the thought that this was the same overture that played out in the lime-sized brains of those sauropods plodding across the equatorial bracken of a fragmenting super-continent, moments before the sky exploded and atomized their hides.

Each time I'd look towards the bar, I'd sense the boy's attention drifting off along the same humming tether, and the pangs in my stomach would worsen.

Finally grabbed him by the hand and wove through the crowd until we found my cousin. Asked him to stay put with them, but he protested. He knew. At least he sensed something of my intentions in his own gut, and he insisted on coming along. But when I ordered him to stay, his deferential nod exposed to me for the first time that I was a parent, and that frightened me like never before.

Nor did it feel strange when, for the first and final time, I kissed him on the head and told him I loved him before setting off across the field towards the beacon.

Lee's place was a scattering of solitary regulars eye-fucking invisible partners, and into this hot, damp stuffiness I stepped. Guzzled back a mouthful of sloppy-second smoke and dirty-dishwater stink, and felt oddly more honed because of it. Starfish of all colors and sizes abscessed from the stony face of the bar. Behind it idled Lee, palms on the counter, deltoids high by his ears where a cigarette was nestled, bearing already trained at the door. The lights pinged off the bottles behind his shoulders in a grandstand of quasars.

As our eyes antlered across the room I could feel my smile twist to ape his, and only then did I truly see the familial resemblance between him and the boy—so much greater than between him and Jenna.

My insides thawed and stabilized at last, I hooked my thumbs into my belt-loops and gave him the underside of my chin.

Before coming around from behind the bar to meet me, the sprightly, eager warrior actually slipped the cigarette from his ear and into his mouth.

*

When we'd gotten home from the store and I mentioned to Jenna that we'd run into Lee—that he'd given the boy a starfish—she dropped to her knees and mimed a gruesome, silent scream to the ceiling.

She'd been in the kitchen baking, and the tears that avalanched from her face cut fresh canyons through the strata of flour on her smock. No sound issued from her however, and for several seconds it was as if all the air and heat had evacuated the room. Then she started shrieking.

Not him! Not him! Not him!

The final *him* transmuted into a low bestial moan, the expulsion forcing her body forward onto her forearms in a pastiche of prayer. Her forehead ground against the floor as if pestle to mortar, her whimpering mounting steadily until her voice could no longer corral it, whereupon she started to bash her head repeatedly into the terra cotta tile.

My gravity regained, I pounced on her and rolled her off the floor into an embrace against the wall. Blood from her yawning head gash weeping onto my shoulder, I struggled to grasp her wrists as they flailed for the boy, crying out, imploring to him in a desperate breaking-voice whimper—*Don't go in the attic, baby! Don't go in the attic, baby! Don't go . . .*

Sought out the boy and found him huddled on the seventh step of the stairs, staring through the balusters at the countertop where Jenna had been making sugar cookies. The dough, as always, had been cut into all manner of cosmic shapes, and for the first time I sensed the skulking reason for why the star pattern was never used.

*

Peering out the police car, past Lee's bar and the yellow blanket covering his body on the gurney, I wonder if the mole cricket will right itself or not. As the cops hauled me off the curbside, I kept tapping my toe next to it, the decision fighting me to the very end. But there'd been enough mortality for one night. Enough reparation.

They did the favor of lighting Lee's appropriated cigarette for me at least, genuinely shaken by the sight of my mutilated hands, certainly in conjunction with having first viewed what remained of him inside the bar.

Glancing up at the sky, my shattered, handcuffed hands still blazing, I behold the last falling star and make a wish. A hope, really—that balance need not be just an aspiration, and that acceptance is the true endgame of it all. The way I see it, I've paid handsomely enough for the love I've taken in this world. For this I seek no absolution, nor offer apology.

*

Seven years behind me, and a few yet to go.

All that is mine are the figures perched on the sill of my little cell porthole and across the bolted sliver of poly allotted for books and postcards; tokens the boy wrapped diligently beforehand in gunny and twine on all those hazy Sunday visits before his schooling ensued in Junes and Januaries. His plastic and rubber testaments to all the things he loves and reveres and hopes, and even those things he fears though he doesn't yet know why, like the lonely soldiers, and the lonelier superheroes, and the ill-fated T-Rex's and saber-tooth tigers that sometimes, when the sun runs ornery and wallops a hole in the clouds, visit as life-sized fossils poured through the tiny porthole upon my concrete world. Tributes to Plato's allegory. But that penance is mine, and not the boy's and not his mother's—that pretty redhead who took me when I wouldn't take myself, and who asked me one day if I would bring steaming and crying into the world this infant she knew haled not from my faulty genes. And yet I played the part because she still looks at me through the glass like none other has or will again. Like I'm some fantastical creature spun from the ether to someday bear once more upon its shoulders the boy that isn't my boy, but the man's whose glow I smothered during a mutually beneficial fulmination. Because the father can't play the grandfather, any more than two bodies can fill the same space, and only one of us could claim the gravity that anchors Dale to this diorama, at least till it gets refashioned by the next runaway bug, global skirmish, or fiery pebble from the cosmos.

$$\Omega$$

Final Dispositions
by Linda McCullough Moore

My family is deciding what to do with me. I am the oldest sibling. Always have been. I thought the years might mute the effect of that, but nothing so far. I have been, and I remain, the reason why the siblings take each new birthday with some measure of aplomb. *Well, I'm still 4, 7, 14 years younger than her.* I, the comfort toddy.

They hold disposition meetings. I am not invited, but I read the minutes of the meetings in the awkward silences and the odd questions during the phone calls that follow each conclave. *"How do you feel about Texas?" "Do you mind the cold?" "Do you have any special friend who lives in a big house,* (pause) *with a trained nurse?"*

I don't mind this actually. I am quite pleased at their level of involvement. There were decades when I think that they forgot I was alive, or if they remembered, they forgot I was their sister, or sister-in-law . . . a friendlier affiliation by a mile.

"Invite me to the meetings," I say to my brother Paul. "I promise not to voice opinions or spill brown liquid anywhere it shows. I'd like to know just what sort of thing might be under consideration."

"No," he says.

I like his style. The others would have said, "*What meetings*?"

Paul got whatever integrity was floating in our gene pool.

"I might be able to help," I say encouraged by his candor.

"I don't think so," Paul says.

"Are you sure you've saved no money whatsoever? This would be my sister Irene—I mean Eileen—on the phone. I like it that I can never keep her name straight. It gives me hope.

"Zero money?" she says,

"Oh no," I say, "I saved a bundle. It's. Just. That. I. Spent. It. All."

Each word seems worthy of it's own personal sentence.

"Tom is coming over Tuesday morning. Please write that down. I'll wait." My sister says. She pauses. I mime writing "Toooosday, Doomsday" on the palm of my hand. "Tom's taking you for a ride."

"I'll be ready," I say. "Don't tell me what time. I like to be surprised."

"Ten o'clock. Wear stockings, Margaret," she says. "Wear shoes."

"Okey-doke," I say. "Okey-dokey."

People think that *crazy* is achieved when one day the gale force wind makes one final violent tear and your little craft slips its mooring. Oh no, it is achieved by you, who one knot at a time untie the tethers, whimsically at first, and then to some or sometimes no known purpose. You write a shameless letter to a friend who has blown you off once and for all time and say with no shame, *Why don't you like me? Did you ever?* You offer up the tidbits that will be the stuff of ridicule for certain, you pass them out to members of your family on a tray like some peculiar, worrisome hors d'oevres.

*

Eileen's husband Tom rings the doorbell. My siblings would have done the same. To walk right in would signal an affinity they neither feel nor seek.

"Would you like any sort of carbohydrate?" I ask. He is still standing on the porch. He never comes in unless it is a national holiday, and then it must be one celebrated across the board, not just by Jews or Christians or the tree people.

"I'm good," Tom says.

"I have no doubt," I say, "but are you hungry?"

"Oh . . ." The question catches him off guard. He clearly doesn't know the answer. It is one most often decided for him by Eileen.

"Why did you marry her?" I say.

"Who?" He is still busy with the last question.

"Oh yes," I say. "I had forgotten. You were married once before Eileen."

"I wasn't thinking about that," he says, rather simple, even for him.

"No," I say. "I wasn't thinking of her either. You never talk about her."

"Well, we should be on our way."

"Maybe I could go live with her, your first wife. Let's see, I'd be the sister-in-law of her ex-husband," I say. "Stranger things happen every day. A lot of them to me."

"Do you want a coat?" Tom says.

"No," I say. "I've got a closet full of them. But thanks."

He gives me a frightened stare. The man would not know humor if it wore a nametag.

"Well," he says, clearly with no heart whatsoever for the project. "We should be on our way."

He is so dutiful, it makes his skin sag.

"Why are you doing this? Tom, this is your life. You could be dead by nightfall. A lot of people will be, and you could be one of them as easy as the next person. Let's forget about wherever Eileen wants you to take me. It will only be a waste of time. They won't admit me. It will turn out they only take retired Presbyterian clergy. Or, Paul won't want to pay for it. Or, they'll have a waiting list. Or, at the last minute I'll kick the bucket. If this is the last day of your life, trust me when I tell you, you will want to have spent it some other way no matter if you end up in hell or heaven."

"I don't believe in hell."

"Well there you go."

It's the first nearly interesting thing I've heard him say since he met my sister.

"What was she like?" I say.

"Who?"

"Wife one. Eileen's predecessor."

"I don't remember." Tom says. "I've been married to Eileen for nearly thirty years."

"I'm sorry," I say. I am too. I always thought he was born this way, never thinking what it might do to a person to be married to Eileen.

"Why did you marry her?" I say.

"Oh, I was young." He makes it sound a rather unusual thing to be. "I was young. And she was beautiful."

"Eileen?"

"Janet Royer." His voice is just about a whisper. "Janet Helen Royer. Look, we really need to go. Eileen has made an appointment for you."

My sister is forever and a day, making things for people, appointments and decoupage, Rice Krispy treats and bright fabric snakes you're meant to keep your plastic bag collection in.

I grab my pocketbook and slam the door behind me.

"You want to lock that?" Tom says.

"I do not," I say.

*

It takes me fourteen minutes to locate Janet Helen Royer on Google. First I typed in "ex-wives." Four billion, one hundred and six results. Then I tried her name which reduces that number by about four billion. Turns out she illustrates books for dyslexic children. Actually somebody else does the art and she does the illustration using words instead of pictures. They are called word books.

It seems she draws words under the pseudonym of Janelle Roy—not the most profligate use of the imagination, but I allow for the possibility that she makes the most of what's she's got, a habit I refuse to despise. I send her off an email to say my six-year-old dyslexic son Leroy reads her illustrations with great pleasure as does his auntie Eileen Conway (just in case Janelle Roy is a woman given to putting two and two together).

I issue myself a poetic license: I do not have a son named Leroy, or any other name, but if I let my childlessness figure largely in every single email I send off, I might as well downgrade to dial-up and be done with it.

Janelle Roy (aka Wife One) sends an e-mail in return. She wishes me every joy, which strikes me as being a bit over the top, but I prefer it to a curse, and let it be. The imprint at the bottom of the e-mail says that she will be giving a reading of her words at a *mall near you.* That is to say, near me. I click on the bar that says *Find a Mall near you,* hardly troubling to fret that Mall is capitalized, only to find the Mall (maul?) is even nearer than I thought.

I call Eileen to arrange a little rendezvous with her hubby's previous wife. Stir the pot a bit. The answering machine picks up. Eileen hasn't answered her phone since that little fiasco the day Tom took me to the perpetual care place. How was I to know she'd paid 140 bucks for the evaluation. How was I to know she'd sent me there to take a test. A person should be told these things. Now she's terrified no place will have me. As though I'd want to go to any place where people were excluded on the basis of how strenuously they agreed or disagreed with statements like: I am not worried about the future.

I leave a message for Eileen. "There is an author reading from a book, *The Idiot's Guide to Nursing Homes*," I say. "Tuesday night at 7 at the mall in Coudersport. Could you drive me? I could take the bus, but I didn't know if you wanted me appearing in public unchaperoned. Plus, if the bus crashed and I didn't get killed, but only severely maimed and injured, we'd be worse off than we already are."

Eileen picks up just as I am finishing the final phrase.

"Hello," she says.

"Hello," I say.

"Who is this?" she says.

"Who is this?" I say.

And we're off to the races.

*

Eileen drops me at the main entrance to the mall. I allow it. I really can't walk as well when I am with her.

There's a old man standing by the door with a collection can, yellow, labeled in bright red, "For the Retarded," the sign says, which I take to mean he's working freelance. The organized prefer *developmentally disabled*. I don't know. *Retarded* seems more hopeful some way. It's nothing permanent or cast in stone, but more a matter of speed than anything. Timing. His progress is only retarded, slowed a bit, delayed, but coming, oh yes coming certainly. Just not today. *Retarded* gives a person something to look forward to.

*

"Well, I must say that was a good evening." When Eileen found out I'd read the listing wrong, her sincere pleasure at my having made a mistake was enough to sweeten the whole night.

Eileen and I are shut back up inside the brand new Japanese container that we will travel home in, or if not, that will transport us to our long home.

"Long home." I say the words out loud. They sound portentous driving off together into the black night. "Have you ever heard the phrase *long home*, referring to death? Or, I guess, to where death takes us to?"

"Don't talk about death," Eileen says. "It's morbid."

"Duh," I say, the word *Duh* being one of the three innovations of the last half century that are really worth something, the other two being e-mail and breakfast all day at McDonalds. I don't go to McDonalds, but I like knowing that if I did, I could get a fried egg sandwich in the middle of the afternoon.

"I don't know why you have to work death into every conversation," Eileen says. "Don't think I didn't hear you mention it to that woman tonight, the one with those oxygen tubes in her nose."

"The way she looked, it seems to me it would have been impolite not to mention death. And don't say you didn't sense the general amazement that she was still alive when we went to get our coats. Trust me, death's on everybody's mind, at least four times a day."

"Not mine," Eileen says. "I concentrate on happy things, like the nice books this lady was showing tonight. Her drawings were beautiful."

I wonder would she be calling her a lady if she knew the author was the one woman in the universe she'd shared a husband with.

"What did you think of her?" I say.

"I thought that if she needed oxygen, perhaps she might be more comfortable at home than in a bookstore."

"I didn't mean her," I say. "I meant what did you think of the author?"

"Some day you will appreciate what I am trying to do for you, Margaret."

"Don't hold your breath," I say. "Get it, it's an oxygen tank joke. But what did you think of the author?"

"Why do you care?"

"Because she was Tom's wife."

Damn. I wasn't going to tell Eileen that, or not until we had invited Janet Helen Royer, aka Janelle Roy, to a few Thanksgivings. See, this is why I am no earthly good at card games. I cannot keep a secret for two minutes in a row.

"Tom who?"

She's asking for form's sake. She knows Tom who.

"Your Tom."

"But Tom's first wife's name was Janet, this woman was Janelle."

"Uh, that's not exactly DNA."

"You knew it was her. You brought me on purpose. You told me it was a book on nursing homes."

"Eileen, what person in their right mind would drive 25 miles on a school night to get the author to sign a book on nursing homes."

"I'm gonna' tell," Eileen says and suddenly she is four and I am eight, and neither one of us has even heard of Alzheimer's or knee replacements or long term care insurance. The only thing in fact we know of human tragedy is what goes on inside our family.

"Who you gonna tell?" I say, but already I am warming to prospect of our reporting all the crimes committed on the planet to the proper authorities. I want to take Eileen by her thin, clammy hand, her diamonds hurting both our fingers in the tightness of the grip. I want to pull her out of the car and drag her down the street for blocks, calling out to strangers on the way, "Police station, where is the police station. Is that it?" and pull her with me through the heavy doors and grab the sleeve of the first policeman that we see and say, "Come quick. I need you to arrest our parents. They are scaring us to death, and when we are old women we will put each other into nursing homes and into unnatural situations in book stores in shopping malls. Malls. Malls. Places where people go so they won't have to think about death. Oh never mind! Just come. You need to lock them up and throw away the key."

"Remember," I say to Eileen, in a voice gone hoarse from all the yelling that I should have done a half a century ago, "remember the night you started to take Freddie downtown to the police station, to show them the belt buckle welts, the places where the tip end broke the welted skin?"

"Oh Margaret. That was in another lifetime."

"No. No, it wasn't. It was this same lifetime. This same one we're living in tonight. There is only just the one."

"Well," Eileen says. "I never got there. I met Grandma Chase at the corner and I told her where I was taking him, and she told me to go back home and to never, never tell a living soul, or God would punish me."

A different God from that crawls into the backseat, as we stop for the light.

"I was just trying to help," Eileen says. "I was just trying to do the right thing, with Freddie. I was just trying to save his life."

"Tell her she did." It's God, in the backseat.

"You tell her," I say to Him.

"Nah. She's gotta' hear it from you," He whispers in a raspy smoker's voice.

"You did save Freddie's life," I say.

God clears His throat, and makes a "Go on" motion with his index finger.

"I mean, look at him," I say. "Look at Freddie's marriage. Look at his kids. Look at their kids. He's had practically the best life I know."

"Yeah well."

"Yeah well, why do you think that is?"

"Well . . ."

"Hello? because of you."

I know she gets it. When a thing is true, you don't have to explain. I turn around to wink at God.

He's gone. Off to save some other sisters. It would take him all night just do one neighborhood.

"And I *am* just trying to help you," Eileen says.

"I know," I say. "And I was just trying to help you, taking you to meet old Janet Royer tonight at the bookstore."

"No, you weren't," Eileen says as she pulls into my driveway, a little closer to the holly bushes than she might have liked.

"No, I wasn't," I say.

I open up the door.

"Did you forgive them?" I say. "The parents. For what they did."

"Yup," Eileen says. "I did."

She gets out then and walks around the car.

"And do forgive me?" I say.

"Nope," she says, and takes my hand and pulls just hard enough to make my standing up a thing that I can do, then lets me lean, pretty hard at first, on her arm as we go up the walk. "Not in this or any other lifetime," she says.

*

There's a priest in my kitchen. If I had to go to church to confess my sins, I'd spend my whole life in the car driving there and back and wouldn't need a nursing home or any other housing.

No matter that my priest is one I have concocted out of equal parts of worn black shiny cloth and Holy Fathers born in Hollywood. He is just as unforgiving as the real thing. Forget the fact that I have purged the fey Bing Crosby, long lines of priests in handcuffs on the evening news, fabled Fathers that my Catholic friends curse after they have lost their faith or seriously misplaced it: mine is no more efficacious than the fat man who waddles to the altar at St Michael's every morning, even public holidays.

Still he is my confessor. There are agents in our lives we do not choose.

"Forgive me Father for I have sinned," I mumble as I open up the freezer and taker out a bag of frozen cherries. "It has been three hours since my last confession."

He's silent as the night.

I wait him out.

"Okay, okay," he says, "what did you do this time?"

I keep him on retainer for the reason that he has less patience than I do.

"I took my sister to a book store for the express purpose of cutting her down to size. Or, at the very least, of annoying the hell out of her."

"And did it work?"

"Nah. Hardly."

"So you are guilty of the sin of wasting time created by the Eternal One."

"That too."

"Are you sorry?"

"Sort of. I wish she had gotten really angry and thrown her purse at my head and forced me out of the car by the side of the road on a dark and stormy night, the avenue awash in burglars and other men in urgent need of immediate incarceration."

"*You can't always get what you want.*" He sings it. He is a priest who if he ever moved beyond the walls of this my kitchen would play guitar in church and make the host be sour dough. "You want to be punished for your sins," he says. "There is no penance in the book for sins against the sister. And so there can be no forgiveness."

"Eileen just told me that tonight."

"And she an atheist," he says, "a card-carrying member of the club that says that sin is only mental illness, mental flu, mental TB, mental appendicitis."

"But we know better."

"We know worse," he says. "Sin's the best hope we've got. If it's mental, all we've got is pills and they stop working the day that you stop taking them. Ah, but sin . . ." his voice softens, "sin can be named and napalmed. You gotta' love a God who's up to that. Your problem is you always wanna' save yourself."

It's sermon that I've heard before.

"So, what would you say to giving me a few Hail Mary's here?"

"They only work when you are penitent. And then they only sandblast sloth. What we need here is a Savior."

He shakes his head and for the first time I notice that his hair falls in gentle waves onto his shoulders. "I always thought that you were bald," I say.

"I'm not," he says. "You never really look at me."

"I never really look at anyone. Could I offer you a cherry?" I hold out the bag.

"They're frozen," he says, and grabs the bag of designer potato chips from the bread box, and sits down at the table to read the paper.

I don't know what the priest is your kitchen is like. Mine is a slave to carbohydrates.

*

I take my glasses off and move my face six inches from the mirror on the wall. My eyebrow is a composite of so many sorts of strands. I am absorbed. Time stops for my eyebrow inspection, as time will, if ever you are lost inside a moment. Time stops and waits, and then you look away and time starts up again.

That's how I come to know there is eternity.

*

I'm lying on the floor. And in this slim interval between bemusement and the stark desperation I am planning, the room has become all ceiling. It's wider than the floor, and the room is one of those odd shapes you study in geometry but never come across in your real life. There's lots of real life on the floor.

The underbelly of the antique carved desk my grandmother wrote her grocery shopping list upon is nothing more than what appears to be a piece of Masonite. And exactly where have I pulled that mid-century word from? I take no small amount of comfort from its having come to me so easily. I do not think a person calls back the word *Masonite* if she has had a stroke.

I take it also as proof definitive I have not lost my mind. I give myself these periodic evaluations. A person likes to know just where she stands. Or in my case, lies. I will assume I have not hurt my head. I find out some extent of the damage though, when I try to drag me, soul and body, one so heavy, one so thin, across the kitchen floor. I left the telephone up on the kitchen counter when I immigrated to the floor, and now they're telling me it is a one-way trip I've taken.

The light has moved from the front porch to the back deck when I awaken next. Cold. I'm mostly cold. And I am sad and clutch the sadness like a ragged baby blanket I've uncovered in a bureau drawer. It's faded, ragged, aged by time and overuse, but it is there. That's the main thing. If I am sad, if sad is something I can still be, then it will be all right.

The next time that I waken, it is dark. But darkness happens, it occurs to me, once every day. The next time that I awaken Eileen is beside me with a magazine. She's sitting in a chair. Her make-up isn't working for her. Any shade of orange will just betray you in the end. The floor I'm lying on has gone all soft and white and warm and I am loving lying here.

"I was sad," I tell Eileen. "I was cold, but I was sad."

"Oh Margaret. You're awake. We were so worried. How do you feel?"

"Fine," I say. "Nice and warm." I don't say it, but the sadness is all gone. Now I will have to see just how I am to live with that.

*

"Life is so short these days."

The words are whispered in a voice I do not recognize, out in the hallway, whispered by a person I don't know; although, it would probably be good for me to spend some time with a person who says such things without a twisted curl, a single saffron thread, of irony.

Irony, mother's milk to me, but at the end of the day, it doesn't make a twiggy twig of difference. It's not how you view your life, it's what happens in your life that matters.

Right now, what's happened to me matters a great deal. I have a heart that let me down, as I have long suspected it might one day do. It actually stopped beating. Tell that to the lady in customer service when you go to get my money back.

And when that happens and you live to tell the story, they demand it be a good one. Even strangers in blue-spotted nightgowns sliding down the hallways holding on for dear life to some rolling pole, transparent plastic bags in full sway, asses veiled from public view by the strength of loosely knotted ties, even they, arrest their snail-creep, stop the rolling poles, and say in voices manufactured down in intubated airways, "*What was it like?*" "*Did you see a bright light?*"

I tell them what they want to hear once they have told me precisely what that is. They are not shy about requests. Then it's just a matter of a spattering of *yeses* and the odd *no*, and a great deal of shaking of the head. "Did you see a great white light?" "Why, yes I did." "And was it the brightest thing you ever saw or hope to see?" "It was," I say. "Were you amazed?" "Why, I still am."

"Is there hell then?" A former Christian missionary, who has come to write her final chapter as a nurse, asks me, standing at the trash chute to the incinerator. "Is there hell?" she says.

"Oh yes," I say.

"I thought so." She upends her schoolroom metal basket, sending something sounding like a bowling ball with spikes on it, crashing down the chute. "I thought so," she says. "But you never know."

"No," I say. You never do."

Like I say, I give people what they require of me. Actually, I do know though. I have seen what does await us. The whole thing. There is good reason that we are not told. There is good reason why we cannot tell what we have seen and why the white light is so popular in stories resurrected people tell. White, the color of no story. Blinding-light transparency, the opposite of truth.

Everybody asks what is it like, everybody but Eileen. Her, I would tell.

*

My new home is a kennel. No matter that every dog in the whole place is registered and has had all its shots. I call it the kennel club. It drives Eileen nuts.

"They give us dog food for lunch," I tell her. "In dog dishes. With dog silverware."

"Oh Margaret, stop it. They've got paella on the menu for tonight."

"Don't let them fool you. That's code for mussel shells in red food coloring broth. Woof, woof," I bark.

Eileen sets about tidying up the room which she keeps tidied up to within an inch of its life.

"Eileen," I say. "Sit down. Stop fidgeting. Take a pill. Read a book. I have a copy of *Great Dog Expectations* I got from the pound library."

She doesn't take the bait. She knows me well enough to know another fifteen seconds and I will be so sick of dog jokes I'll never bark again.

"It is awful," I tell her. "Here," I say, in case there's any question just where awful is.

I've not felt sad one moment since they brought me here the day I left the hospital.

Eileen comes to visit dutifully, but she comes, far more often than I'd visit her. I'm pretty sure.

*

I have a dream and in the dream I am in kindergarten and Eileen is my grandfather. And everyday she walks me to the school and sits outside the schoolhouse door on an old wooden, backless bench, sits there until school is over and then she walks me home. I wake up feeling safe as that. But sad, not safe, is what I want to feel. Safe means there's harm and danger out there, just on the other side of that thin window pane. Ah, but sad, sad means there is love, to be missed or had, and lost and maybe had again, or if not, at least to be longed for, missed and reminisced and carried in you in a place where safe has never been. Sad is the deep of feeling. Sad tells a person that good is.

And here I am, arrived at the asylum, I who always thought that safe was everything, and only now the telegram bearing this insight as new information gets forwarded to this address, carried by the last delivery man on earth, on the day before the world ends.

*

Eileen wants me to sign a power of attorney, a sheaf of papers to declare that she can forge my signature on anything she wants to and never spend a single night in jail.

"No," I say. That's the long answer. The shorter answer is the silent one. The terser refusal is my faking palsied hands. I lift my paws, gone claw-like in pantomime, let one side of my mouth droop, my eyes bug out and stare.

"It isn't funny," Eileen says.

"Are you enjoying this?" I say

She scowls.

"No," I say. "I'm serious. I honestly hope that you are getting something from the roles we have been cast in here. You are well and strong and truly married, and I am enfeebled in this frightful way, and I just hope you feel the muscles of that victory. Living well, that best revenge."

"I'm not looking for revenge," she says, her shoulders slump, and I would write a check with lots of zeros on the money line if she could be all spit and vinegar again, the little bony girl, all fire and spine who told our brother Tom that he could fly if he jumped off of the armoire, who said ice cream will come from the light socket if you wet you finger and you put it in the socket. That girl I begged our father to beat one Sunday afternoon for her nefarious infractions, and when, finally near nightfall, he did, I wished her strong enough to turn on him and slay him. We had a King James English childhood with verbs that could rear up on their hind legs and scare tall men. I want Eileen to be as powerful as she seemed then. As mean.

"You want revenge," I say.

"No, Margaret, I don't," she says. "I'm too tired for revenge. You want revenge."

"No, I don't," I say and tell us both a thing we didn't know before.

"Do you think that we will ever be friends?" I say. "You and me."

"We're sisters," Eileen says.

I know she's right.

"We could be friends if you would change every single thing about you," I don't say to her, she doesn't say to me.

We sit pretending it were possible if want were there, when we both know that we will not be friends until we find ourselves on *that* day discovered and forgiven.

*

My doctor tells me that any dream you have that is not in the middle of the deepest, most lickety-split-eye-moving phase of sleep is an hallucination. I don't know what to make of that. I'll ask Eileen. The question would be a whole new thing for us. We never speak of anything you cannot photograph.

Sister talk.

We are not living, we are being lived.

As they say.

*

I'm pretending I am dead. It makes a change. There are few amusements left to me. I've even tired of magazines. I lie not breathing on the bed, mouth gaping, staring eyes. Until I blink. It's probably just as well I never took up acting.

The matron enters on her clicky shoes. I call her *the matron* in my mind, like some housemistress shrew whom Dickens dissed, or would have if he'd thought of it.

"And we are how this morning?" the dragon lady says.

I don't answer. I'm pretending she is dead.

"Cat's got our tongue," she says.

I see this boiled tongue we were just about to slice and serve with serious mustard and a sturdy stein of Old Peculiar Beer, being pounced on by an enormous tabby who, fierce fat feline though she be, can do little more than gnaw one corner.

"Eeeewwwe," I say involuntarily.

"Do we have a problem?"

"Any number I should think," I say. I'm old and you're mean, for starters. I don't say it. I'm a big fan of the obvious speaking for itself.

"Well, we will take care of you." A threat if I ever heard one.

Eileen peeks her head around the door. Have I ever been so glad of her appearance.

"May I come in?" Eileen says.

"No," the matron says, more brusquely than even she might have chosen. "No, I'll come out. If you don't mind,

I'd like to have a word with you. We don't mind do we?" she says to me.

I lie back, pretend to be dead. No one appears to notice or to care.

"We will be moving her today," the matron's voice carries from the corridor as she must surely know it will. Her voice is noisy, like her shoes. She must have been an irritating child.

"Moving?" Eileen says.

"Yes, dear. It's time. We must accept these things."

Who's this we, white man? As Tonto said to the Long Ranger when the Comanches appear.

"Moving where?" Eileen's staying focused here. I like that.

"Upstairs, dear. To the Sunshine Unit." Good grief, we're back to second grade and everybody knows that *The Bluebirds* is a euphemism for the kids who'll probably never learn to read.

Sunshine Unit.

Even the name is scary.

"But my understanding is that the higher floors are for people with bigger problems?" Eileen can sling euphemisms with the best of them. "Margaret's mind is clear as it ever was."

"Dear, she's incontinent."

Shit! I didn't want Eileen to know. I did not want Eileen to know. I so wanted her not to know.

"A secretary that I work with is incontinent." Eileen's voice is matter of fact. I had forgotten. She looks at life with a less impassioned eye than her incontinent sister.

No matter. I hate to have her know. To have her thinking of that every time she looks at me. *She's leaking. She pees herself*, our mother would have said, whispering derision.

"Dear, we have to accept that there will be more changes."

"My name is Mrs. Ferguson," Eileen says.

You go girl!

"Well, Mrs. Ferguson, dear, we need to accept little changes along the way."

Little changes. They're shipping me to hell.

"She's fine right here," Eileen says. "She's fine here."

"And she will be fine upstairs, dear."

"Well, she won't be going upstairs," Eileen says. "She won't be."

"Dear, you have no choice."

"Actually," Eileen says. "I do. We have decided that my sister will be leaving Pine Brook."

"And where will you put her, dear?"

"We will not *put her* anywhere. She will be coming home to live with me. We have been planning this for quite some time."

Hallelujah! I feel a sweet and certain sadness start up at the bottom of my toes and fill up all of me. Sadness everywhere. Sadness I have sought in every hiding place.

"Well, I think you will be surprised to learn just how difficult your sister can be."

"I will not be surprised at all. It's a thing I knew about before you were born."

Cue the angels. Blow the pitch pipe.

Eileen appears around the corner. She's one determined girl scout. "Let's pack your things, Margaret. We're getting out of here."

"Whatever you say, Sparky."

*

Eileen carries a small overnight bag filled with what I need tonight.

"We'll be back for all her things later," she tells the matron who stands at the front door trying to look as though her life has meaning.

Eileen takes me by the hand and drags me past her, and there is no grandmother on the planet earth who will stop her this afternoon, no force in hell or heaven who would dare to try.

"Well, good luck, dear," the matron says as we pass by.

"My name is Mrs. Ferguson," Eileen says, icy, stern.

"So, should I call you that too?" I say and squeeze her hand as she all but drags me across the parking lot.

When Eileen's grandson was very little I took him to the movies, and the only movie not sold out that afternoon was THE MADNESS OF KING GEORGE III. Driving home that day I asked the little boy if he had understood the movie. "Sure," he said. "The people said, 'God save the King,' and at the end of the movie, God did."

130

"Mrs. Ferguson," I say as Eileen crawls into the driver's seat and buckles in. "I like the way this ends. I like what this ending does to the whole story."

"Don't call me Mrs. Ferguson."

Eileen puts her foot down and the car jerks forward. The whole way home she pumps the gas pedal, up and down. It's how she drives, it's how she's always driven. But tonight I think, she'll get us where we need to go.

*

"Final Dispositions" originally appeared in *The Sun*, and was anthologized in *The Pushcart Prize XXXV* and the author's collection *This Road Will Take Us Closer to the Moon.*

Ω

Ma Writing
by Robin Stratton

In my 54th year I discovered that my mother was a better writer than me. She had always been supportive of my career, telling friends with pride that her son was a novelist; NO, NOT PUBLISHED, I'd hear her say, BUT MOST OF THE GREATS AREN'T. Which was what she'd heard me say. I even convinced her that not winning a Pulitzer Prize carried more prestige than winning one, asserting in my ridiculously imperious voice, EVERYONE KNOWS IT'S BULLSHIT. Why she put up with me all those years, I have no idea. I was jobless and single and prone to upper respiratory complaints no matter what the weather.

For years I got up when she did and wrote for eight hours while she was at work, but when she retired four years ago our days became less structured, beginning with a tendency to sleep late and indulge in a generous, unhurried breakfast. Rather than chafing under her sudden steady presence, I enjoyed it. I brought her to my favorite antique books store, and accompanied her to the supermarket. Our new loose schedule allowed for walks after supper and watching television until midnight, eating popcorn or ice cream; cohabitating like an elderly couple, and comfortable in long silences while she knitted scarves for orphans, the needles clicking rhythmically. Conspirators in the sham that all was perfectly normal in our world.

During a particularly nasty bout of writer's block where I hadn't produced anything worthwhile in more than six months, she approached me with a story she'd written. She said maybe I could find some use for it. It was ten pages, carefully printed with no cross outs, in the same tidy hand-writing that used to alert the school secretary that I'd be home sick that day.

"I'll take a look," I said reluctantly, wondering how I could tell her tactfully that her writing wasn't good.

But it WAS good. I saw from the first sentence that she had IT—*THAT* rare, indefinable agility that marks some writers as "great." Her language flowed with an easy skill that I had not achieved even after years of study and effort; each word was powerful and honest, every scene sparkled with the most vivid imagery I had ever read. The storyline was exceptional, featuring a cast of fascinating characters, a unique set of circumstances, and an ending that brought tears to my eyes, something that had never happened to me.

"Ma!" I said.

She paused in her knitting and smiled. "It's quite good, isn't it?"

I didn't answer as I read it again. The way she juxtaposed parallel plots was nothing short of genius. The primary event came upon the hero so unpredictably and with such devastating potential ramifications that even upon my second reading, I couldn't wait to get to the end to see how it turned out.

"How long did it take you to write this?" I demanded. I won't deny that after my initial shock I felt sick with jealousy. Her talent was obscene! Where had it come from?

"I wrote it last night," she said. "Do you think you can use it?"

"Use it?"

"Yes."

"What do you mean?"

"Send it to one of those magazines. Pretend it's yours."

"I can't do that!"

"Why not?"

"Because I didn't write it." It was with great effort that I remained calm; what I wanted to do was stomp both feet and shake my fist at the ceiling and shout at God, SEE? THIS IS WHY I DON'T BELIEVE IN YOU! I couldn't even move from my chair, and the fire behind me crackled like applause upon the threshold of her fame.

"Oh, honey. It's almost as if you did. I've been listening to you for years. You taught me so well. There's not one thing in there that you couldn't have done yourself."

I shook my head. "You wrote it. You should get the credit for it."

"You think we can get it published?"

"Are you kidding? Any magazine would kill for this!"

"Send it out, let's see what happens. If someone wants it, then we can talk about whose name goes where."

Meaning she was going to let me have it. For a long time I sat wrestling with my conscience. I knew this story would sell. It could be the beginning of my career. And didn't I deserve some success? After all those years of struggling? Maybe Ma was right, maybe I'd had some influence over her, and it was because of me that she'd been able to write this.

"I'll send it out to a few places," I said. "We'll see who wants it."

*

Everyone did; from the most recipe-riddled women's magazines to elite literary journals whose prose was so densely intense that I didn't even understand it. A bidding war ensued, and I decided upon THE PUTNAM REVIEW, a fancy, semi-snobby New York-based magazine that bumped an article by Sir Raymond Seavers in order to include my story in the very next issue. On the day Ma and I opened it and saw my name there, my guilt diminished like a light bulb in the sun. "See?" she said, "I knew you could do it!"

She stopped eating ice cream so she could fit into her old cocktail dresses, and began hosting parties at the house; small at first, then larger and noisier as friends brought friends who brought friends. I attended them sporadically, spending much of my time sipping champagne in New York with the world's finest authors and publishers. Pretty soon there was talk of adapting my story to the big screen for a lot of money. The best part was, I didn't even have to write the script—people in Hollywood would do that. And at the end of the year I won the Sheila M. Wentworth prize, the only single-published author ever to do so.

After the holidays the excitement died down, and my new agent, a woman of such daunting sophistication that I could not have approached her under any other set of circumstances, began hounding me for another story.

It was, of course, the thing I had been dreading most. I still lived with Ma, and as the days went by the question hung in the air thicker than the smoke from her fried liver: COULD SHE DO IT AGAIN? I didn't feel right asking. In fact, since that first night we had never discussed that it was she who had written the story, not I.

A week later I walked into the kitchen and saw a stack of pages on the table next to my plate of eggs and sausage.

"I wrote a new one," Ma said cheerfully, flipping pancakes. "Have a look."

My hands were trembling as I reached for it. PLEASE PLEASE PLEASE BE AS GOOD . . .

It was. Again, her brilliance astonished me, offering a totally different story, every bit as engrossing, and with new characters that were even more interesting. She nailed scene after scene, and I was bedazzled by the writing. The ending hit me with such impact that I actually let out a gasp.

"Should we send it to the same magazine as before?" she asked.

"No, I have an agent now. I'll send it to her and she'll do all the work. Jesus, Ma. How the hell . . .?"

She smiled. "Thank you."

I watched as she slid pancakes from the pan onto a plate. Humming, she served me six, herself two, and sat. A simple woman who'd been a cashier for most of her life; who'd never traveled beyond two states to the south and one to the north. Married for two months to a man I'd never met, hairdo unchanged for 40 years, dyed black now. How had she . . . that's when it hit me: Maybe the writing wasn't hers! Maybe she'd found some obscure text and copied . . . oh God, all those trips to the antique books store! "Ma!" I heard myself say with an abruptness that startled her.

"What?"

Did I really want to know? I took a deep breath, tried to decide. Wasn't it possible that she did have this talent, but it had been buried deep until I released it after years of talking to her, no, TEACHING HER, about writing? I met her eyes; for a moment, our gaze locked. I looked away first. "Nothing."

*

My agent loved the second story even more than the first, and sold it right away to a much fancier magazine. More rave reviews, and this time I wound up on the Letterman show telling him how it felt to be an overnight sensation. He asked where I had gotten the idea for such an incredible story, and I said WHO KNOWS? and the audience laughed. One of the fans who approached me after the show was a beautiful, educated woman in her 30s. After an embarrassingly brief and unsubstantial conversation, she accompanied me to my hotel and spent the night. This soon became my pattern when I traveled—be on TV, meet women, then sleep with them. But I never allowed myself to develop feelings for anyone, because letting someone into my life would mean letting them in on my secret. And I could not do that.

The movie of my first story was released and received stellar reviews. BEGUILING AND COMPELLING said THE LA TIMES. Ma's parties resumed, more boisterously populated than ever. On the sly, she got a face lift.

Before I knew it, six months went by and again I felt pressured to come up with another story. Ma and I went about our days not talking about it. All I could do was wait.

When she handed the stack of pages to me one evening, I sank into a chair, weak with relief, and started to read.

This one was significantly longer, and phenomenal in every way, with outstanding characters confronting complicated and suspense-filled circumstances. I marveled at the writing, the language, the elegantly-crafted sentences. One of the main characters died so tragically that I had to blink out tears before I could finish reading.

"Are you okay?" Ma asked.

I nodded. The plot was so gripping that I found myself racing to get to the end; the situation seemed so out of control, it didn't seem possible that it could pull itself into a satisfying resolution. But it did.

"I thought that one came out particularly well," Ma said.

I felt sick, the culmination of two years of jealousy and guilt and fear. "Did you really write this?" I heard myself ask.

Ma's eyes opened wide. "I beg your pardon?"

"You heard me! Did you write this? Or did you copy it?"

"How dare you!" she sputtered.

I stood and waved the pages in her face. "No one can write like this! Where are these coming from?"

"I told you! I wrote them!"

"Ma! You couldn't have!" I forced myself to sound understanding and reasonable. "Just tell me the truth. Where are you getting these stories?"

She looked at me for a long time, then said, "I never thought I would live to see the day my own son calls me a liar."

"MA."

"Why won't you believe me when I say I wrote them?"

"Because how could you? You went 74 years without writing a word, and now this? It's insane! You copied it! You copied all of them!"

"I did not!"

"Why won't you tell me the truth?"

"I am!"

Drained and ashamed, I dropped back onto the chair. Ma and I had never shouted at each other, never. I'd been a quiet, well-behaved child; as a teen I studied most nights instead of going out drinking. There'd been no girlfriends.

I'd gotten decent grades, attended a local college, and never moved out or got a job; Ma said STAY HOME AND WRITE. So I did: novels, short stories, poems, screenplays, more novels. And thirty years went by like a shrug.

"Okay," I sighed, "if you say you wrote them, then I have no choice but to believe you."

"Thank you," she said in a stiff, resentful tone that didn't go away for the better part of a week.

*

This time the story was translated into five languages. Universities started using my writing as the new benchmark for quality. Inspirational speakers contacted me for quotes about staying focused on my dream and never giving up. My agent was bombarded with calls from publishers who wanted me to pull together a compilation. GET MORE STORIES TO ME AS FAST AS YOU CAN, said her message on the answering machine. I looked at Ma.

"I'll need a few days," she said.

Of course the book was a hit and sold millions of copies. I was invited to teach classes, which I declined, claiming it would take too much time away from my own writing.

A few months later my agent called about an article in the NEW YORK TIMES. "I don't want you to panic," she said. "This always happens."

"What always happens?"

"Oh, these so-called experts who claim that anyone good is a fraud. Bunch of academics with nothing better to do than try to derail your life. It's jealousy, plain and simple."

OH GOD, OH GOD. "What are they saying?"

"That you didn't write the stories. That the style is too, let me read the exact quote: THE STYLE IS TOO AUTHENTICALLY VICTORIAN. Can you imagine? They say they've reviewed your college papers and nothing you've ever written looks like this. How ridiculous! College was a hundred years ago!"

"I . . . I . . . so what should we do?"

"Wait it out. They claim they're going to expose you. Bullies! But what they don't know is that this will only make you more famous."

"I have to go," I said, hanging up before she could say goodbye.

*

That night I awoke from a nightmare with a jolt and a yelp. Chased by a monster or something cliché. Still shaking, I got up, headed for the the bathroom. When I stepped into the hallway, I saw that Ma's light was on. I tapped on her door. "Ma?"

"Uh, just a minute." I heard rustling; the sound of a drawer being opened then closed. "Come in," she said.

I opened the door and saw her lying in bed. "What are you doing up, Honey?" she asked.

My eyes went to her nightstand. There. That's where the book was that she'd been copying. SHIT SHIT SHIT! "I had a nightmare," I said.

"Oh dear. Was it scary?"

"Well yeah, that's what made it a nightmare."

"Poor baby. Have a glass of water and try to go back to sleep."

"Okay." I shut the door. But then I opened it again, in time to see her reaching for the drawer. She pulled her hand back. "Ma, what are you doing up?"

"Oh, just looking at some . . . recipes."

"Recipes?"

"Yes."

I stood for a solid minute, begging her with my eyes to tell me the truth. But she poofed up her pillow then lay there wearing an expression that was pleasant and helpful. Finally I said, "Goodnight," and closed the door.

*

Then came the coveted Prentiss Award. Ma and I had adjoining rooms at the hotel and she looked beautiful in a full-length teal gown. She'd had her hair and makeup done by professionals who came right to her room. Resplendent with pride, she admired me in my tux.

I took a deep breath and blew it out slowly. "Ma," I said, "I'm going to tell everyone that I didn't write those stories."

Her smile took a long time to fade, then she looked bewildered. "What?"

"I can't live with the guilt."

"Oh, honey," she said, "Why spoil this? We've got a good thing going."

"I can't stand it, it's making me sick!"

"Don't be silly." She adjusted my bow tie, patted my shoulder. "No one will ever find out. And we're not hurting anyone."

I pushed her hand away. "We're hurting ME, Ma, I'm hurt! I'm sick with guilt! I can't live this way! I'm going to tell them tonight what's been going on. I'll say that you were just trying to help, and . . ."

Rage took over her expression. "Don't you dare!" Leaning close, she lowered her voice and I smelled hotel room-issued mouthwash on her breath. "If you say one word I'll deny it. You understand me?"

"I have to, Ma. I can't stand it."

"Be smart! All your life you've wanted to be a famous author. It's the only thing you ever wanted! The other boys, they wanted to play baseball or be policemen or firemen, not you! You wanted to do your writing! You didn't care that everyone said you were an oddball . . .!"

"People said I was an oddball?"

"My point is, why make trouble? Why won't you let me give this to you?"

"Because it's not right!"

"But we both got what we wanted!"

"I don't understand, Ma. What did you get?"

She touched my face. "To see you happy."

I shook my head. "It's over."

"Don't you do this!" she said. "Don't you do this to me!"

I knew if I stayed she'd convince me to accept the Prentiss, so I opened the door and stepped into the hall. "It's time to tell the truth."

"I will not let you do this!" she shouted.

I walked to the elevator and pressed the down button.

"Where are you going? Wait for me!"

"Take a cab!" I got into the elevator. The doors closed.

I stood in the foyer greeting distinguished guests; writers I'd admired and gotten to be friends with. The ceremony would begin soon, and Ma hadn't arrived yet. She wouldn't boycott it, would she? Or make a scene? I was shaking; dizzy and nauseous. How long had I dreamed of being a famous writer? My whole life. Like Ma said, the only thing I'd ever wanted.

Suddenly my agent appeared. She put her hand on my arm and in her eyes I saw agony. "There's been an accident," she said. Your mother's cab . . . I'm so sorry."

*

After Ma's funeral I went back to a house that was so empty, so quiet. On the floor, an ever- growing pile of sympathy cards—not just from her many friends, but from people in the publishing world too. All sorry for my loss. My grief was deep and unrelenting for months.

But eventually the healing process began, and one morning I awoke ready to know. I got up and walked into her room. Opening the drawer of her nightstand, I saw a small hardcover book, obviously old, lying face down. In a daze, I watched my hand reach for it and turn it over: IDEAS FOR WONDERFUL STORIES said the title. I opened it and saw notes along the margins in Ma's handwriting: MAKE EVERY WORD A POWER WORD!! WEAK MODIFIERS MAKE YOUR WRITING SOUND IMPRECISE!! SHOW DON'T TELL!!! All things she'd heard me say over the years; my tips, my hard-earned knowledge. True, she'd lifted some passages from the book word for word. But most of the writing had been hers. And mine. I closed the book and put it back in the drawer. She was right, no one would have found out, and we weren't hurting anyone. And we'd been happy, so happy.

$$\Omega$$

My Father's Ghost
by Lee Wright

My father's ghost sits next to me on the porch of the old hunting cabin as the last day of summer seeps into the dry ground. The muggy air is thick with mosquitoes and the sickly-sweet stench of vegetable rot unique to Appalachia in summer.

Inside the cabin, it's always the past, always a great time to be a man. Out here however, I am forty years old, overweight, and balding. My wedding ring lies beneath a pack of cigarettes in the breast pocket of my sweat-soaked work shirt. I'm sure I can feel the metal pressing against my chest with each beat of my heart, but that's probably just another of my bittersweet poetic delusions. Or maybe I'm just drunk.

I fish the last bottle of beer out of the cardboard six-pack beside my chair and open it using the rusty opener nailed to porch rail.

The yard is overgrown—waist high and brambly in places—and stinks of wild onion. Even the wide gravel driveway is almost lost to the forest. And then there's the kudzu. It eats everything. It swarms over the rusted shell of the old F-100, climbs the rails of the porch, shrouds the roof of the cabin, and creeps in the windows. The weed is relentless, tenacious, inexorable, and, in its own perverse way, beautiful.

My father lights another cigarette. He's maybe forty-five, heavy around the middle, and not quite a decade from the heart attack that will put him in his grave, but the hands are the same as they were the first time they held me: hard, rough, and strong, the jagged nails yellowed by nicotine.

"A man's got to have his own place," he says quietly, almost as if talking to himself.

I stand and my back cracks just the way my father's used to. I toss my cigarette into the brown weeds at the end of the porch. I can smell rain in the air and, somewhere beyond the valley, thunder rumbles.

"Does it hurt?" I ask my father's ghost.

He looks at me for a long time, his face all but lost in shadow. Finally, he nods almost imperceptibly. "We don't talk about things like that—especially in a place like this."

I smile. My dad, possibly fearing his own restless potential, usually talked only sports and Louis L'Amour novels. They were safe subjects and he knew them well.

In the darkness, I can't see the smoke at the end of the porch where the cigarette smolders in the dead grass, but I can smell it.

Holding onto the leaning, splintery rail, I ease my way to the overgrown gravel driveway. You'd need a 4x4 to drive all the way up to the cabin now so my little convertible—probably the only thing I'll get in the divorce—is parked up by the highway. It's a long walk in the dark, but, already, there is light behind me, flickering, dancing, lighting my way.

Ω

Puddles Like Pillows
by Suzanne Conboy-Hill

Things began disappearing round about March. Just little things—a newspaper left on a bench, or a sandwich wrapper—and not blown away or tumbled into a corner, just gone. We shrugged collectively: so rubbish vanished—was that even a problem? Then somebody caught an empty beer can in the act and started squawking about it; how it went, like, straight up in the air, man, he said. Wasted, the rest of us said, because he wore big trainers and a hoodie. But almost overnight, YouTube was stuffed with videos of everything from paper clips to small toys vanishing into the sky. Just the ones left outside, mind; the ones indoors stayed put same as always.

After a while, with the streets and parks getting less cluttered, it started to look as if some cosmic recycler had dropped by to tidy us up. So then people stopped using the bins and just hung about with their cameras waiting for their banana skin or whatever to take off. Pretty soon, though, the yawn factor set in, what with the gazillions of uploads and the conspiracy theories, so eventually only little kids, grannies, and the seriously un-cool stuck around to watch any more. From there, it was only a small step to becoming a kind of unspoken utility and people began throwing litter out of their windows to save lugging bags and bins around. This meant you had to watch out for flying items which, when everybody got a bit blasé about it, could be anything from old phones to dead flower arrangements, some of them still in the vase. One man was killed by a sofa landing on him from the twenty second floor and its owner complained to the council about how it was their goddam fault because it never woulda happened if their goddam collection system hadn'ta broken down.

We went on like this for quite a few weeks, with small inanimate objects on the outside of buildings heading skywards and everything else staying put. Then one day a miniature Chihuahua was seen hovering at the end of its ten metre extending lead, yapping like they do and its owner yapping too, and people standing around hooting and yawhawing and filming it for posterity. This was about the same time NASA got involved, but it wasn't because of the Chihuahua, it was because the ISS had been hit by a fountain pen, captured on video as it penetrated one of the external storage tanks. The gaseous discharge from the gigantic hole it left propelled the station out of orbit and now it was following Voyager into deep space with a trail of domestic debris behind it so it looked like a fourth grader's collage of a comet.

Not long afterwards, bigger items like bikes and deliveries of wine in twelve bottle cases began disappearing straight upwards, and stuff that hadn't moved before because it was indoors, started bumping up against people's ceilings like birthday helium balloons. The ceiling became the go-to place for your missing credit cards and car keys, assuming you hadn't already lost those by leaving them to one side at a cash point or on top of the car roof at a filling station. For a while, the sky had been full of jangling black dots, clacking plastic that flipped and tipped and reflected the sunlight, and fluttering paper money birds. Now it was full of fridges, those big Marshall amps they have at music festivals, and parking attendants' huts that hadn't been fully bedded in.

Chimney stacks, solar panels, large marquees, Smart cars, and Honda Civics went next, prompting a rush on the weightier Saabs, Four-by-Fours, and ex-army personnel carriers. Roofing experts worked over time, some of them entertaining the crowds by catching floating tiles and hammers while they hip-hopped along their scaffolding. And a new breed of specialist, claiming a hot line to The Rapture, started spamming everyone with texts about how, for a donation of only one thousand dollars, they could ensure you got a place in the light—never mind that it wasn't people that were vanishing, or that the Rapture-ists themselves were struggling to find a rationale that suited their purpose and had gone very quiet about it all.

When it rained, it rained very slowly and made puddles that looked like pillows.

People bought magnets, lead weights, and bits of cast iron and put them in anything moveable to keep it still. Old sea anchors were at a premium, and individuals carrying a bit of excess poundage hired themselves out to sit in things that might be vulnerable to a sudden uplift. One idiot tried to buy heavy water for his fish pond and got arrested as a terrorist. He'd still be on remand if it hadn't been for the jail disassembling upwards, brick by brick.

Once all the buildings and bridges were gone, along with the cattle and sheep and shrubs, and the boats and submarines and whales, there were only a few of us left—all clinging to trees that were slowly up-rooting, like we were in a massive flood with a current that was sucking every-thing along to some great overhead ocean.

For a while I had a kind of a neighbour; a woman in a purple skirt dangling upwards from a sycamore tree a few hundred yards away in what used to be our park. When it creaked and shattered and gave way, she went with it and I thought she'd yell or something but she didn't make a sound. I can't see anyone else now and I'm hanging here thinking I might be the last and wondering what I should say to mark the occasion: *So long and thanks for all the fish? Always look on the bright side of life (ti tum, ti-tum, ti-tum-ti-tum-ti-tum)?* It ought to be something profound—

Oh crap . . .

*

"Puddles Like Pillows" originally appeared in *Zouche Magazine*.

Ω

Pull a Titus

by Ashley Shelby

At lunch, everyone was telling old station tales about the ones who went crazy: the guy whose girl had dumped him, how he'd loaded a sledge with graham crackers and beer, slipped the straps over his shoulders, and walked out into the polar night, heading for Vostok Station. The lady scientist who went on a vodka binge one night and had to be carried over the electrical foreman's shoulders to her room because everyone at the bar had deemed her too irritating. The woman who was caught and disciplined for blowing a guy in one of the bathrooms and was caught again, that same night, blowing another guy.

Cooper knew she was a confession away from becoming South Pole Station lore herself, and so retreated to her studio and turned to her canvas empty, almost blind, where there were no distinct shapes anymore, only malformed bodies and the vague notion of color. She knew she'd be left alone, everyone else at the station assuming she'd gotten toasty, so when Doc Carla, the only one who knew, poked her head in Cooper's studio, she assumed she was getting the doctor's inevitable welfare check.

But when Carla sat down across from her, Cooper heard, "It's time."

The options were these. One: telling Vapcraft officials in Denver about the situation—and Carla told Cooper that she was obligated by contract to have already let Denver know, but fuck Denver—and seeing what was possible on their end. The definition of "what was possible" was never offered; a flight out from the station in mid-winter was impossible. If you winter-overed, you knew this going in. You signed papers to this effect. You agreed before going on the ice that you wouldn't attend your parents' funeral if they died back in the States during the polar winter, that you would try very hard not to mortally injure yourself because if you were going to die, you were going to die at the Pole, not on a Medevac flight to Christchurch. So what was "possible" coming from Denver could be nothing but a recommendation to the National Science Foundation never to give Antarctic Artists' Grants to thirty-year-old substitute art teachers with a history of bad decisions.

Option two, Carla told Cooper, was letting it run its course, with no prenatal care, no vitamins, and no fresh vegetables, and zero sunlight, and getting off the ice on the first flight out in August.

Option three was preceded by a chapped hand removing a filthy knit cap that read "Hard Truth Medical Centre" and a substantial pause, and it was letting Carla terminate the pregnancy. "No, I am not authorized to do it," Carla said. "Yes, I let Denver know before I came down here that I had done pro bono work for Planned Parenthood and was trained to do the procedure, and yes, they were horrified at the idea that Washington would catch wind and yank our funding. Fine. I get that. I signed the contract that said that. However," she dragged this last word out and leaned forward toward Cooper. "My Hippocratic obligations sort of trump my contractual obligations to Vapcraft. I don't want you to die."

That afternoon, Cooper lingered in the library, where the pictures of winter-overers through the years hung in cheap frames. She peered at the faces in the images. They seemed cheerful, even ebullient. But hidden among the freshly winter-overed would be a face or two that was expressionless, drawn, eyes open a little too wide.

And then there was the portrait of Titus, the first hero from the Scott expedition, the lonely monk in a J.Crew sweater. There was something in that dim look of profound pessimism that overtook his features as soon as the shutter closed. He'd hated Scott. Thought him incompetent. And yet he'd stepped out, taking a blind, limping walk to his death, barefoot, to keep Scott from perishing. And yet, he'd done it.

*

It sort of went without saying, among the old mystics and seekers in the early centuries, that family life was incompatible with the highest forms of spirituality. You couldn't be a prophet when you were just Jesus of Nazareth: competent carpenter and attentive son. You couldn't spend a week under a Bodhi tree trying to achieve Final Liberation when you were sporting a wife, a newborn, and meddling parents. Cooper understood this; when she was home, caught in the scarred tentacles of her family, it was impossible to be anyone but Cooper Gosling. At home, she was ridiculous. Away from home, she could be heroic. And she and her father, Bill, had this hero-thing covered. They winter-camped in the Boundary Waters Canoe Area Wilderness in December; they ice-climbed the river bluffs in late January (with Cooper belaying, naturally); and they read aloud to each other Cherry Apsley-Garrard's Worst Journey in the World.

Bill was the kind of guy who would shove a book into your chest and give it a couple pats for emphasis, and say: "You must read this." Rejection of these recommendations came easy to Cooper's older sister, Billie, because she didn't care; for Cooper, though, rejection was out of the question. She couldn't afford it. And so she accepted the reading assignments the way a novice camper tried frantically to keep the kindling smoking. It was in this manner that Cooper had managed to slog her way through Everyman's Library of the World's Most Boring Books. So when Bill had urgently pressed both volumes of The Worst Journey in the World into her open hands, her expectations were low, despite the promise of the author's awesome name.

By the time the horses had to be brained on the ice floes to keep them from being devoured by killer whales, Cooper was consumed. She became obsessed with knowing how long it had taken Titus Oates to die in the blizzard into which he'd walked. A day earlier, his frostbitten foot swollen to three times its size and completely black, he had asked to be left behind. Scott and the other men on the expedition refused. He begged. They put him to bed in his sleeping bag. That night, he prayed to die before morning. When he awoke to find he was still alive, he decided to do it himself. When Titus walked into the blizzard that morning, he didn't bother to put his boots on.

"That is a man," Bill had said, tapping the photo of Titus in the book. "Remember that when you're thinking about settling down. That is what you look for."

It was implied, of course, that Bill Gosling was a man, perhaps the last of his breed, and given his ability to rake a roof in a Minnesota blizzard, tan a deer hide in the backyard, and drag himself a mile through Gates of the Arctic with a concussion and two broken ribs, Cooper had no reason to disagree.

And winter. Jesus. In winter, a faint madness had always replaced Bill's otherwise lucid psyche. Winter existed, for everyone in the family—except Dasha, their mother, who didn't get involved in the bullshit—solely to be survived and, if things went well, to be bested. They were a hardy family. They grew up here, after all, in this funny milk-pitcher shaped, lake-studded state. Cold weather made Cooper and her older sister, Billie, bold. Instead of contracting like metal, they expanded with winter weather, matching it step for step. They didn't hide from it, or shut it out; they joined it. At least Cooper did.

"Snow is one of the best insulating materials, if used properly," he could be relied upon to say before making a winter camp in the backyard of their suburban Minneapolis home. On these occasions, he'd pull a black ski mask over his head, a fur-lined Eskimo hat on top of that, and strap a hunting knife to his left calf. "The quickest way to die is to stop paying attention, Cooper."

The night before her flight to Christchurch, New Zealand, the take-off point for the Pole, Bill had handed Cooper the reading copy of Journey they'd shared. "Pull a Titus if you have to," he'd said.

*

"I want my freckles back," a girl from Fuels said at the 90 South bar above the galley the next day.

"I want to see a bird," someone else added.

"I want to smell a new book."

"I want to fondle a fresh bell pepper, and then eat it."

"I want to go barefoot."

"Slushies in ten minutes," someone in a greasy, blackened parka shouted from the door. Slushies were booze parties held out in the Dark Sector, where the scientists—the Beakers—worked, and were different from the other drunken parties because the drinks were mixed with Antarctic snow, not ice from the ice-maker.

Bozer, the head of construction, pushed his ice-wife off his lap and arose from his recliner. He grabbed an old Coleman cooler off the floor and a bottle of Maker's Mark.

"You're going?" one of his friends asked, doubtfully.

"The fuck," Bozer responded.

"You are not at your best when you socialize with the scientific staff," his ice-wife said.

"I'm spreading my wings. Learning to trust again. You coming?" The construction staff all looked away. They hated the Beakers and the Beakers hated them, but Bozer liked booze, and he loved the way it tasted at Slushies.

"What say, cupcake?" he said to Cooper. "You want to visit God's bar?"

*

The sun used to be blazing when Cooper would arrive at the lesioned mouth of the dome. The ice crystals in the atmosphere made it look like a runny yolk, but now it was gone, disappeared over the lip of the earth. Front-loaders and coughing Caterpillars still crept over the ice behind the main station in the mid-day darkness, though, carrying construction materials and enormous drums of solvent and human waste.

As she and Bozer slogged their way down the entrance tunnel, Cooper glanced back at the clinic, where the doctor had biopsied herself a few seasons earlier. It would be at least as horrible, Cooper thought. At least. Cooper knew the tiny comma was going to unfold soon.

Outside, once they'd moved beyond the red glow of the exterior lights of the station, the darkness was complete, seemingly as final as an equation, and the wind came in scalding waves. The plateau beyond the station was crisp and antiseptic. Halfway to the Dark Sector, Cooper saw

Bozer's flashlight beam waver for a moment, then disappear. It took her a moment to realize he was on his hands and knees. He ran his battered mitts over the snow tenderly, and dropped the Maker's Mark into the snow.

"This is where I want to take my last drink." Cooper watched as he began scooping the beautiful snow into the Coleman, icicles hanging from his moustache like tiny opaline tusks. He looked at Cooper through his goggles and said, "Don't tell anyone. It's my secret."

Bozer was an asshole, had been one from day one, but he'd always been honest. It was Bozer who wore the t-shirt around the station that said "Fuck Science: This is World-Class Construction." So Cooper asked him, "You ever feel like pulling a Titus?"

"Fuck does that mean?"

"You ever feel like walking out into a blizzard and never coming back?" After a beat, Cooper heard a rusty laugh that seemed to freeze and shatter in the air, like water thrown from a galley pail to impress the new kids.

"You don't come to the ice to commit suicide, honey," Bozer said, closing the Coleman. "You come here so you don't." Looking at him, in the low illumination of the flashlight, Cooper could see nothing beyond his frosted-over goggles, just the promise of two eyes, as crystalline as ice, staring back at her own half-erased face. It looked like the only face in the universe, and the blistering loneliness of life washed over her. Bozer shoved the Coleman at her. "Keep walking, cupcake."

Pulling her eye mask back over her face, Cooper threw herself headlong again toward the Dark Sector, toward the scientists and the answers and the whole wounded continent.

*

"Pull a Titus" originally appeared in *Thirty Two Magazine*.

Ω

The Road to Hana

by Midge Raymond

Again they're arguing even before they leave the hotel. Ethan lets the door shut behind him, and Sue contemplates staying: Let him get to their rental car, start the engine, and wait. Or would he leave the resort, hit the Piilani Highway, head off to Hana without her? Perhaps she shouldn't test his loyalty, not today.

Still, she lingers for a few moments, just long enough to make a point. She wanders through the oversized suite, checking that the lights are off, the hair dryer unplugged, a luxury she does not have at home as she ushers their two teenagers out of the house, then wonders later whether her own stove off. She pours a glass of water, drinks half of it, then finally pockets her key card and goes downstairs.

It takes her a moment to find Ethan amid the palms overflowing in the open-air lobby. "Do you have the camera?" she asks as they merge onto the two-lane highway.

"Yes."

She looks at him. His eyes are on the road, his jaw set. "Let's just forget I ever mentioned anything, okay?" she says, referring to their argument.

"I'd like to," he says.

"Then why can't you? We're here to celebrate our anniversary, for God's sake. What happened with the ring was thirty-odd years ago. It didn't have anything to do with you."

"I think it does."

"It's just a ring, Ethan. And it's not as if another man gave it to me or anything."

This elicits a humorless laugh. "I think I'd actually prefer *that*," he says.

She sighs and looks out the window. "Do you know how to get there?"

"The map's in the side pocket, in the guidebook."

She opens it up, looking at the zigzag of lines representing the road to Hana. "Listen to this," she says. "'The Hana Highway is fifty miles long. Thanks to its hairpin turns, blind curves, and the eight- to ten-hour day it entails, the Road to Hana is often called the Road to Divorce by couples who dare to embark upon it.'"

She catches his eye, timing it just right. They both begin to laugh.

"Let's stop in Paia for breakfast," she suggests. "We'll need our strength."

"Okay," he says. "Whatever you want."

She leans over and kisses his ear. He turns toward her, and she pulls away. "Eyes on the road!" she says.

"Relax. We haven't even reached the hairy part yet."

He's right; Sue sees that the serious zigzags start after Twin Falls. She hopes it's not as bad as it looks.

*

Along Paia's strip of surf shops and seaside cafés, they walk past windows awash with surfing gear and beachwear until they encounter the only open restaurant, five of its six tables full, its air moist and redolent with brown sugar.

After they order, Ethan leans back in his chair. "So, did you bring it with you?" he asks.

She looks at him, surprised. "Why?"

"I didn't see it in the safe when I put my laptop in."

"I don't want to start another fight."

"I know," he says. "Let me see it."

She touches the ring, in the front pocket of her shorts. "Promise you won't get mad?"

He nods.

She holds it between her fingers for a moment—an antique, of white gold, with five meager diamonds enveloped in its flowery arcs and swirls. She hands it to him.

He holds it up, inspecting it. "I can't believe you brought it with you."

"I still don't see why it upsets you."

He places the ring on the table, between them.

"I was in high school, for God's sake," she says. "Until a few weeks ago, I completely forgot I had it."

Their meals arrive, enormous plates of fruit and eggs and potatoes for which Sue suddenly has little appetite. She picks at chunks of pineapple and watches Ethan eat. He holds his fork, as always, with his fingers over the top; he sips coffee while still chewing. Twenty years of marriage, of sitting across the breakfast table from this man, and she still can't grow accustomed to his habits.

Yet as far as bad habits go, Ethan has few, though his reaction to the ring had been a surprise. At this point in their marriage, Ethan no longer notices if Sue has a new outfit or haircut, but for some reason, the night before, he detected the ring immediately when she slipped it on as they were heading out for dinner. Perhaps it was because they were away from home, or because it was their anniversary—for whatever reason, the ring seized his attention, even before Sue's new dress, or the updo that had taken her half an hour to perfect.

Ethan reached for her hand. *I've never seen this before.*

I've had it since I was a kid.

It doesn't look like a kid's ring. Where'd you get it?

Don't worry, she said. *It's not a gift from a secret lover. I'll tell you over dinner.*

At the restaurant, she waited for the wine before she began, then she paused to order an appetizer. She found something strangely exotic in the telling—in the promise of having a story, one that had nothing to do with their daughters or the school board, the latest software launch at Ethan's company or Sue's dwindling real-estate commissions—it was simply a tale about herself, long ago, during a time when she was not yet defined by her work or her marriage or her children. It was astonishing to her that she'd forgotten about the ring, which she discovered in a long-sealed box while cleaning out the storage room a few months earlier. It was even more astonishing, and somehow thrilling, that after more than twenty years of life with Ethan, she was about to tell him a story that he'd never heard before.

And so she wanted to prolong this undercurrent of mystery that normally eluded them, even when they did manage solo evenings out together. But after she told him, a new, dreadful feeling replaced it: the question of how, after decades with Ethan, she could so horribly misjudge his reaction.

"Aren't you going to eat anything?" Ethan interrupts her thoughts. Her breakfast is still untouched.

She shakes her head. "You know, it's just a piece of jewelry," she says.

Ethan sets his fork across his empty plate. "Jewelry always means something."

"Not when you're a kid."

"Sure it does. I read about a girl who escaped from North Korea using her mother's bracelets. Now she's safe, she's in the States, but she still wears dozens of bracelets on her arms, in case she needs them again."

"That's different, obviously."

"You've kept the ring all these years," he says. "It must mean something to you."

She checks her watch. "We should get back on the road."

*

As they cross to the eastern side of the island, the sun ducks behind rain clouds, and large drops intermittently hit the windshield. Ethan turns up the radio, masking the silence in the car.

Sue had put the ring back in her pocket. She'd brought it with her this morning thinking that she'd leave it at one of the stops on the Road to Hana, for someone to discover, or that she'd toss it into the sea. She feels the need for a ceremonial parting.

She remembers when Brooke Wheeler first wore it to school, during their junior year. It was an heirloom from her grandmother, a gift for Brooke's sixteenth birthday. All the girls coveted the ring, huge on Brooke's tiny, graceful hand.

Sue hadn't had a chance to try it on, as many of the other girls had. She wasn't a friend of Brooke's and could never have hoped to be; the two had nothing but gym class in common. Then, one morning when Brooke took off her ring before volleyball, Sue watched her leave it on the wooden bench in the locker room, so preoccupied with her friends, her hair, that she forgot all about it. Alone in the locker room, Sue picked it up. She turned to follow Brooke to the court; she would return the ring, become a hero, and never again be ignored by Brooke and her coterie. Then she changed her mind. If she returned it later, after Brooke had panicked and searched and mourned its loss, she would be an even bigger hero.

Nearly giddy with the thought, she stashed it in her locker. Brooke laughed with her friends, unaware of what she'd lost. It wasn't until after they'd all showered and changed and Brooke went to don the ring that she discovered it was gone. Then came a loud shriek, a rush of girls on their hands and knees, a trip to the principal's office to report it missing.

Sue helped in the search, though Brooke hadn't seemed to notice. Sue and her best friend, Maria, talked about it at lunch. By then, Brooke was offering a reward.

Probably the janitor will find it, Sue said. *I'm sure it just fell into a crack somewhere.*

Whoever stole it will probably be the one to "find" it, Maria scoffed. *Brooke may be dumb, but she's not stupid.*

Sue regarded her friend, her only friend, a girl as plump as Sue was skinny, as outspoken as Sue was quiet, and just as invisible. Fear rose in Sue's throat, and she pushed her sandwich away. *Well, she couldn't prove anything.*

Maybe she could. I heard both her parents are lawyers.

It was the first secret she'd kept from Maria, the first moment she realized how her life was different with secrets.

Now she looks out the rain-spotted window of the car, at the odd angles of light falling between the clouds. The radio station emits occasional static, but neither she nor Ethan bothers to change stations. She turns to regard her husband, the morning's quarrel still reverberating in her head.

What else are you keeping from me, Sue? he'd asked when he saw the ring on the nightstand, where she'd carelessly tossed it after their argument the night before.

She'd laughed out loud. *This again? Come on, Ethan.*

I can't believe you could do something like this to someone and not think it's a big deal.

Sue, with a lighthearted air she didn't feel, brushed aside his concern. But he waited for an answer. *Okay*, she said. *I swear to you, this is the only evil thing I've ever done in my whole life. Now you know everything.*

Do I?

She tilted her head. *Why are you looking for a reason to fight?* she said. *Is there something you want to say to me?*

He glanced away, and she leaned forward. *That's it, isn't it? Come on, out with it.*

But he only told her that if they wanted to make it to Hana they'd better hurry up.

*

The night Sue had stolen the ring, she stuffed it into a sock at the bottom of her dresser drawer. She switched the ring's home several times, so that none of her socks would go unworn; her mother tended to notice things like that. She grew accustomed to living with the fear of discovery, with the headaches and insomnia that went along with it. She wanted more than anything to return the ring, to undo what she'd done, but she didn't see any way out.

But the ring gave her something that eventually eclipsed the fear and regret—a sense of confidence, of power, a sense that if she could get away with this, she could do anything.

Sometimes, during those sleepless nights, she slid the ring onto her finger, imagining it belonged there. The weight of it on her hand had a soporific effect; she would close her eyes and relax into the elusive calm that preceded sleep. And at the same time, as if her body knew better, she would awaken just before dawn, just in time to hide it again before her mother's knock at the door.

With no other way out, she began to convince herself that she *deserved* the ring, that it was fair compensation for Brooke having gotten more than she did: beauty, wealth, the easy confidence that went along with both. With Brooke's ring ensconced in her drawer, Sue felt as if she were finally an equal, and one day she found the courage to approach Brooke on the volleyball court, compliment her on her serve, and ask for tips.

Brooke invited her to lunch that day, and as Sue followed her through the cafeteria, she would not allow her eyes to rest on Maria, sitting alone at their usual spot. It was an easy transformation, after so many years of longing, but there was no salvation in it. She learned that she was not the only one with a secret, and as she learned of the kisses stolen from one another's boyfriends, the origins of false rumors making their way through the school, she realized that every one of them lived a precarious social existence, their reputations balancing on the sharp edge of inherent distrust. She wished to return to the long empty table she'd shared with Maria, to the safety, if not the glamour, of having one trusted, unpopular friend. But by then, she could not find her way back.

*

Her stomach rumbles, the sound drowned by the music in the car. Sue opens the guidebook to look for a place to stop. Ethan was right; she should've eaten breakfast—now she is starving when he is full, and if she eats now, she'll be full when he's hungry. When freed of the kids and their schedules, they're no longer in synch.

She glances over at him, his eyes on the road, the previously tense look now melted into his features, rounded with middle-aged pounds—which, she's noticed lately, have also been melting. She could feel, the other night when she joined him in the shower, that he is thinner, firmer than usual. *Have you been losing weight?* she murmured into his neck.

He seemed nervous, self-conscious. *Don't I wish.*

She pulled away to study him. *If you haven't been trying, maybe there's something wrong. Maybe you should see the doctor.*

Nothing's wrong, he said, irritated.

I only meant it as a compliment, she said, then realized that the weight might have been coming off for months and she just hadn't noticed. Making love wasn't like it used to be—heated and insatiable and curious—but hurried, dark, mechanical, if it happened at all. Surely this is only natural when busy, dual-career couples have teenagers: when else do you find the time, except in the middle of the night, in the shadows of the master bedroom, in the sleepy haze of those precious hours past your kids' curfew but before your alarm sounds?

Sue lowers the volume to tell Ethan about Twin Falls. "Two waterfalls," she says, "and a lagoon we can swim in. Glad we wore our suits. Turn off at the two-mile marker." She looks up from the guidebook, then grabs his arm. "There it is! Turn there."

He brakes abruptly and swerves into a gravel turnoff, sending her head crashing into his shoulder. "Ouch," she says, and rubs her temple.

A couple of cars are parked to the right, with space for one more. After Ethan maneuvers into the spot, Sue gets out and stretches. "Looks like we have the place to ourselves," she says.

The trail's beginning is wide and flat, a dirt road surrounded by a verdant, leafy jungle. After about ten minutes, they reach a fork. Ethan looks at her expectantly. "Which way?"

"I don't know. I left the guidebook in the car." She holds up a hand to cut off his next comment. "It's too heavy to carry around. I think it's this way."

They follow the path, whose trees and shrubs close in until it simply ends. They can't walk any further without a machete.

Ethan curses under his breath and turns around. Sue is surprised at how quick he is to impatience and frustration. She remembers, shortly before they left for this trip, taking him aside in the kitchen one night after he'd barked at their younger daughter at dinner. He blamed the toll of late nights at work, the lack of good sleep. *We're all swamped*, she reminded him. *The girls and I don't take it out on you.*

He'd given her a long, wide-eyed look. He opened his mouth as if to say something, then seemed to change his mind. He apologized to her and to their daughter, and then went to bed, hours early.

"What's the big rush, Ethan?" she says now.

"We don't have much time here if you want to go all the way to Hana."

"So we don't make it all the way to Hana," she says. "So what?"

He shrugs. "Fine by me."

They reach the crossroads again and set out on the other path, which quickly narrows, the vegetation closing in on them, exposing only the ground under their feet and patches of sky above. As Sue observes the imprints Ethan's shoes leave in the moist earth, and her own next to his, she suddenly feels as if this shrinking trail is leading nowhere she especially wants to go.

The trail slickens into smooth round rocks and mud. They hear the rush of water in the distance. Ahead is a small pool whose waterfall is nothing but a trickle. "Let's keep going," Sue says quickly. She moves past Ethan and takes the lead, stepping carefully on the slimy tree roots, her shoes occasionally sliding into the muck below.

She stops when she sees that her next step hovers above water—a clear greenish pool fanning out before a gushing waterfall. "We made it," she says, relieved. They are completely alone, more alone than she has felt in a long time, and at the moment, something about their solitude feels forbidden.

On a large flat rock, she begins to pull off her clothes. As she steps out of her shorts, she hears a *clink*: the ring. She reaches down to where it has fallen, amazed that she's managed to forget about it. Undressing down to her swimsuit, she lets the ring drop next to her clothing. As she enters the water, she looks back and sees it beside her T-shirt, winking in the sun.

Ethan has stripped down to his trunks but is still standing on the rocks, taking photos. Sue lowers her face into the water, her eyes skimming the surface, and watches him. When he joins her in the pool, she swims over to him, wrapping her legs around his waist. She leans in to kiss him, but he's leaning away.

"What's with you?" she asks.

He doesn't answer.

"You've been acting strange ever since we got here," she says. "And don't tell me it's that stupid ring."

He looks at her, the same wide, steady gaze he'd given her in the kitchen that night. "You're right. It's not the ring," he says.

She shrinks away from him, and as he begins to speak, she lets her face sink into the pool again, half-hearing his muted words as the water fills her ears. She watches his mouth, as if she can see the words form and drift into the air, hovering there in the whitish, late-morning light; she wants them to stay there, to prevent them from swimming into her ears, being processed by her brain—but a part of her knows, in fact fully comprehends, what he is saying. A part of her has known it all along.

"You're a bastard," she says.

"I'm sorry," he says. "I've been trying to find a way to tell you for months. There's no such thing as a 'good time' for this."

"Did you have to pick the worst?" She feels tears rising and quickly ducks under the water, to rinse them away. "Have you talked to her since we've been here?"

He turns toward the rocks. "I think we should go."

"What else do you think?" she shouts after him. "Do you think you're in love with her? Do you think you want to leave me and the girls?"

She watches his body still, his back motionless in the water until it bends slightly toward her. "I didn't say that."

"Then what?"

Then he puts his fingers to his lips and points toward the path. Sue looks up; another couple has just entered the clearing. She isn't sure whether they heard anything, but she doubts it; they're young, probably in their twenties, arm in arm, faces bent together, lips never far apart.

Just then, they seem to notice Sue and Ethan, obviously just as surprised to discover that they, too, are not alone. "Hi," the young woman calls out. "Hope we're not disturbing you. We didn't know anyone else was here."

Ethan doesn't answer, so Sue says, "Not at all."

"I'm Lori," the young woman says, "and this is my husband, Jeff." She giggles. "I can't get used to saying that," she confesses. "We're on our honeymoon."

"Congratulations," says Sue.

"You don't mind if we join you?" Jeff asks, taking possession of the rock next to the one on which Sue and Ethan have left their clothes, the only one not green with moss.

"We were just leaving," Ethan says.

"In a little while," Sue says. He gives her an insistent look, and she relishes his irritation. "One last swim, then we're continuing to Hana."

"That's where we're going, too," says Lori, "though we haven't exactly been on schedule so far."

"This is worth the stop," Sue says. "The water's beautiful."

As Lori and Jeff prepare to enter the pool, Ethan turns to her and hisses, "Sue, let's go. Now."

She whispers back, "You can't have everything you want, Ethan."

"Well, I'm leaving."

"Go ahead. I'll meet you at the car."

He climbs up to their rock and pulls on his shirt, the water soaking through, leaving big dark spots. They'd forgotten to bring towels.

Sue turns away from him to greet Lori and Jeff as they step into the water. She realizes then that she should be leaving with Ethan, at the very least to give these kids their privacy, but having made a bit of a scene she can't go just yet. She watches her husband's back disappear into the rainforest.

She can tell by the faces of her new companions that the tension between Ethan and herself has not gone unnoticed. "Sorry about that," she says. "We're just having a—a disagreement. Not the sort of thing you want to see on your honeymoon."

"It's no problem," Jeff says charitably.

"Yeah," Lori says, "it's totally okay. Nothing can spoil our mood."

Sue is suddenly reminded of her older daughter, who at seventeen is madly in love with the water polo captain at her high school, and she wonders if all young love is the same, if they all believe, as she once did, that nothing can mar it.

"Want to join us for lunch?" Jeff asks. He indicates a picnic basket on the rocks. "The hotel packed it for us—there's a ton of food, way more than we can eat."

With his invitation, the hunger inside Sue reawakens. It's impossible, she knows, to be thinking of food when she's just received the most devastating news of her married life—but there it is, a hunger gnawing in her gut, a sudden emptiness aching to be filled.

"I'd love to," she says. "If you wouldn't mind."

"Of course not!" Lori leads the way to the basket, and together they lay out sandwiches, pasta salad, fruit, brownies. They chat about the island, the weather, the sights seen and still to be seen. Sue begins to relax in their presence, their happiness so complete, the nature of their love so uncomplicated that she begins to forget about her own troubles. She wishes she could stay with them all day, all the way to Hana, to see the wonder of its scenery through their eyes instead of through her own.

But soon Lori looks at her watch and stands up. She gathers the linen cloth they'd spread out in front of them, and Sue reaches over to help. As they pack the plastic dishes and leftover food, Jeff takes another dip in the pool.

"You'll be all wet in the car," Lori calls out to him. He doesn't hear, or ignores her, and she turns to Sue. "Are all men so stubborn?"

"I don't know about all," Sue says. "I know my husband is."

Lori studies the picnic basket for a moment, then asks, "Is the first year really the most difficult?"

Surprised, Sue pauses, hands poised above the basket. "Actually, I think it was the easiest, looking back. It was probably the most fun. The big challenges come later, when you have kids and a house and work and everything else." She stops, then smiles. "Not to worry, honey. It's all good stuff. You'll see."

"I hope so," Lori says, so quietly Sue almost misses it.

Jeff emerges from the pool then, and moments later they start back toward the parking lot together, passing couples and families along the trail. Occasionally Jeff turns back to warn Lori and Sue of bulging tree roots or slippery rocks.

In the parking lot, Sue helps them pack up their car. She glances over at Ethan, sitting in the driver's seat of their own rental car with the door open. She sees the guidebook propped open on the steering wheel, though she doubts he is reading.

Sue impulsively gives Lori and Jeff each a hug. "Thanks for lunch," she says. "Have a great trip to Hana. Enjoy the rest of your honeymoon." She watches them get into their car and drive away. Then she joins Ethan.

He turns the car around, then pauses at the mouth of the lot. "Which way?" he asks quietly.

She looks at her watch: only a few hours of daylight left. They won't make it even halfway to Hana before dark. "Let's go a little farther," she says. She pages through the guidebook. "There's a small town up ahead. We could see just a little bit more before we go back."

They drive in silence. Like the trail to the falls, the road narrows and curves, and they traverse it as carefully as they had earlier, pulling over and stopping when the road recedes to one lane, letting cars pass before tooting the horn and continuing on.

Sue's seatbelt has twisted across her hips, and she is trying to smooth it out when suddenly she stops and clutches her pockets. "The ring," she says. She turns both pockets inside out. "It's gone."

"What?" Instinctively, Ethan slows down.

"I must've left it at the waterfall." She thinks back, remembering its sparkling light from the pool—and then? She can't recall seeing it again after that, but then she wasn't thinking about it.

They've stopped at the beginning of a blind curve, and Ethan waves on the driver behind them. "Do you want me to go back?"

She sighs, thinking about it. "No," she says. "There's really no point, is there?"

*

Sue points to the left, toward a long row of mailboxes. "Turn there."

He flips on the left turn signal and waits. The traffic returning from Hana, heavy and slow, doesn't ease up. Sue watches the approaching cars, examining the faces behind each windshield, mostly couples. She wonders how long they've been together, whether they love each other, whether one of them, or both, loves someone else. Finally, one of the cars stops to let them turn.

"Thank you!" she calls through her open window, then is surprised to see that it's Jeff and Lori, on their way back already. They didn't make it very far either, Sue thinks. Lori seems to recognize them at the same moment, and she lifts her hand to wave. That's when Sue sees it: the silvery flash of the ring, her ring, on Lori's right hand, unmistakable in the late afternoon light. Sue's mouth opens—but she has no words for what she sees.

Lori catches her mistake and lowers her hand. The two women's eyes lock. So this is it, Sue thinks, this is the new fate of Brooke's ring. As Ethan makes the turn and as Jeff and Lori continue on their way, Sue watches the ring disappear, passing again from one woman to another, from one generation to the next, cementing its legacy of longing.

Ethan hadn't noticed Jeff and Lori, or the ring. "Well, we're here," he says, glancing around. "What now?"

"It doesn't matter," she says. "Maybe we should head back."

He doesn't ask why but simply turns around, the gravelly dirt road kicking up dust. Sue rubs her hands together, the right bare, the left still wearing her wedding band—for how much longer, she can't know. She and Ethan join the line of cars returning from Hana, each one close behind the other, traveling carefully from one blind curve to the next.

*

"The Road to Hana" originally appeared in *American Literary Review* as "Twin Falls" and was anthologized in the author's collection *Forgetting English*.

Ω

Saying Goodbye to Yang
by Alexander Weinstein

W e're sitting around the table eating Cheerios—my wife sipping tea, Mika playing with her spoon, me suggesting apple picking over the weekend—when Yang slams his head into the cereal bowl. It's a sudden mechanical movement, and it splashes cereal and milk all over the table. Yang rises, looking as though nothing odd just occurred, and then he slams his face into the bowl again. Mika thinks this is hysterical. She starts mimicking Yang, bending over to put her own face in the milk, but Kyra's pulling her away from the table and whisking her out of the kitchen so I can take care of Yang.

At times like these I'm not the most clearheaded. I stand in my kitchen, my chair knocked over behind me, at a total loss. Shut him down, call the company? Shut him down, call the company? By now the bowl is empty, milk dripping off the table, Cheerios all over the goddamned place, and

Yang has a red ring on his forehead from where his face has been striking the bowl. A bit of skin has pulled away from his frame over his left eyelid. I decide I need to shut him down. The company can walk me through the reboot. I get behind Yang and yank his shirt from his pants as he jerks forward, then I push the release button on his back panel. The thing's screwed shut and won't pop open.

"Kyra," I say loudly, turning towards the doorway to the living room. No answer, just the sound of Mika screaming upstairs and the concussive thuds of Yang hitting his head against the table. "Kyra!"

"What is it?" she yells back. *Thud.*

"I need a Phillips head!"

"What?" *Thud.*

"A screwdriver!"

"I can't get it! Mika's having a tantrum!" *Thud.*

"Great, thanks!"

Kyra and I aren't usually like this. We're a good couple, communicative and caring, but moments of crisis bring out the worst in us. The skin above Yang's left eye has completely split, revealing the white membrane beneath. There's no time for me to run to the basement. I grab a butter knife from the table, and attempt to use the tip as a screwdriver. The edge, however, is too wide, completely useless against the small metal cross of the screw, so I jam the knife down the back panel and pull hard. There's a cracking noise and a piece of flesh-colored Bioplastic skids across the linoleum as I flip open Yang's panel. I push the power button, and wait for the dim blue light to shut off.

With alarming stillness, Yang sits upright in his chair, as though something is amiss, and cocks his head towards the window. Outside, a cardinal takes off from the branch where it was sitting. Then, with an internal sigh, Yang slumps forward, chin dropping to his chest. The illumination beneath his skin turns off, giving his features a sickly ashen hue.

I hear Kyra coming down the stairs with Mika. "Is Yang okay?"

"Don't come in here!"

"Mika wants to see her brother."

"Stay out of the kitchen! Yang's not doing well!" The kitchen wall echoes with the muffled footsteps of my wife and daughter returning upstairs.

"Fuck," I say under my breath. Not doing well? Yang's a piece of crap and I just destroyed his back panel. God knows how much those cost. I get out my cell and call Brothers&Sisters Inc. for help.

*

When we adopted Mika three years ago, it seemed like the progressive thing to do. We considered it our one small strike against cloning. Kyra and I are both white, middle-class, and have lived an easy and privileged life; we figured it was time to give something back to the world. It was Kyra who suggested she be Chinese. The earthquake had left thousands of orphans in its wake, Mika among them. It was hard not to agree. My main concern—one I voiced to Kyra privately, and quite vocally to the adoption agency during our interview—was the cultural differences. The most I knew about China came from the photos and "Learn Chinese" translations on the placemats at Golden Dragon. The adoption agency suggested purchasing Yang.

"He's a Big Brother, babysitter, and storehouse of cultural knowledge all in one," the woman explained. She handed us a colorful pamphlet—*China!* it announced in red dragon-shaped letters—and said we should consider. We considered. Kyra was putting in forty hours a week at Crate and Barrel, and I was still managing double shifts at Whole Foods. It was true, we were going to need someone to take care of Mika, and there was no way we were going to use some clone from the neighborhood. Kyra and I weren't egocentric enough to consider ourselves worth replicating, nor did we want our neighbors' *perfect* kids making our daughter feel insecure. In addition, Yang came with a breadth of cultural knowledge that Kyra and I could never match. Yang had completed grades K through college in China, had witnessed national events like flag-raising ceremonies and ghost holidays. He knew about moon cakes and sky lanterns. For two hundred more we could upgrade to a model that could teach Mika tai-chi and acupressure when she got older. I thought about it. "I could learn Mandarin," I said as we lay in bed. "Come on," Kyra said, "there's no fucking way that's happening." So I squeezed her hand and said, "Okay, it'll be two kids then."

He came to us fully programmed; there wasn't a baseball game, pizza slice, bicycle ride, or movie that I could introduce him to. Early on I attempted such outings to create a sense of companionship, as though Yang were a foreign exchange student in our home. I took him to see the Tigers play in Comerica Park. He sat and ate peanuts with me, and when he saw me cheer, he followed suit and put his hands in the air, but there was no sense that he was enjoying the experience. Ultimately these attempts at camaraderie, from visiting haunted houses to tossing a football around the backyard, felt awkward—as though Yang were humoring me—and so, after a couple months, I gave up. He lived with us, ate food, privately dumped his stomach canister, brushed his teeth, read Mika goodnight stories, and went to sleep when we shut off the lights.

All the same, he was an important addition to our lives. You could always count on him to keep conversation going with some informative fact about China that none of us knew. I remember driving with him, listening to World Drum on NPR, when he said from the backseat, "This song utilizes the xun, an ancient Chinese instrument organized around minor third intervals." Other times, he'd tell us Fun Facts. Like one afternoon, when we'd all gotten ice cream at Old World Creamery, he turned to Mika and said, "Did you know ice cream was invented in China over four thousand years ago?" His delivery of this info was a bit mechanical—a linguistic trait we attempted to keep Mika from adopting. There was a lack of passion to his statements, as though he weren't interested in the facts. But Kyra and I took this to be a result of his being an early model, and when one considered the moments when he'd turn to Mika and say, "I love you, little sister," there was no way to deny what an integral part of our family he was.

Twenty minutes of hold-time later, I'm informed that Brothers & Sisters Inc. isn't going to replace Yang. My warranty ran out eight months ago, which means I've got a broken Yang, and if I want telephone technical support it's going to cost me thirty dollars a minute now that I'm post-warranty. I hang up. Yang is still slumped with his chin on his chest. I go over and push the power button on his back, hoping all he needed was to be restarted. Nothing. There's no blue light, no sound of his body warming up.

Shit, I think. There goes eight thousand dollars.

"Can we come down yet?" Kyra yells.

"Hold on a minute!" I pull Yang's chair out and place my arms around his waist. I realize this is the first time I've actually embraced Yang. While he has lived with us almost as long as Mika, I don't think anyone besides her has ever hugged or kissed him. There have been times when, as a joke, one of us might nudge Yang with an elbow and say something humorous like, "Lighten up, Yang!" but that's been the extent of our contact. I hold him close to me now, bracing my feet solidly beneath my body, and lift. He's heavier than I imagined, his weight that of the eighteen-year-old boy he's designed to be. I hoist him onto my shoulder and carry him through the living room out to the car.

My neighbor, George, is next door raking leaves. George is a friendly enough guy, but completely unlike us. Both his children are clones, and he drives a hybrid with a bumper sticker that reads IF I WANTED TO GO SOLAR

I'D GET A TAN. He looks up as I pop the trunk. "That Yang?" he asks, leaning his large body on his rake so that I have to wonder if he's going to break the thing.

"Yeah," I say and lower Yang into the trunk.

"No shit. What's wrong with him?"

"Don't know. One moment we're sitting having breakfast, the next he's going haywire. I had to shut him down and he won't start up again."

"Jeez. You okay?"

"Yeah, I'm fine," I say instinctively, though, as I answer, I realize that I'm not. My legs feel wobbly and the sky above us seems thinner, as though there's less air. Still, I'm glad I answered as I did. A man who paints his face for Super Bowl games isn't the type of guy to open your heart to.

"You got a technician?" George asks.

"Actually, no. I was going to take him over to Quick Fix and see—"

"Don't take him there. I've got a good technician, took Tiger there when he wouldn't stop digging holes. The guy's in Kalamazoo but it's worth the drive." George takes a card from his wallet. "He'll check Yang out and fix him for a third what those guys at Q-Fix will charge you. Tell Russ I sent you."

*

Russ Goodman's Tech Repair Shop is located two miles off the highway among a row of industrial warehouses. The place is wedged between Mike's Muffler Repair and a storefront called Stacy's Second Times—a cluttered thrift store displaying old rifles, laptops, and steel bear traps in its front window. Two men in caps and oil-stained plaid shirts are standing in front smoking cigarettes. As I park alongside the rusted mufflers and oil drums of Mike's, they eye my solar car like they might a flea-ridden dog.

"Hi there, I'm looking for Russ Goodman," I say as I get out. "I called earlier."

The taller of the two, a middle-aged man with gray stubble and weathered skin, nods to the other guy to end their conversation. "That'd be me," he says. I'm ready to shake his hand, but he just takes a drag from his stubby cigarette and says, "Let's see what you got," so I pop the trunk instead. Yang is lying alongside my jumper cables and windshield washing fluid with his legs folded beneath him. His head is twisted at an unnatural angle, as though he were trying to turn his chin onto the other side of his shoulder. Russ stands next to me with his thick forearms and a smell of tobacco, and lets out a sigh. "You brought a Korean." He says this as a statement of fact. Russ is the type of person I've made a point to avoid in my life: a guy that probably has a WE CLONE OUR OWN sticker on the back of his truck.

"He's Chinese," I say.

"Same thing," Russ says. He looks up and gives the other man a shake of his head. "Well," he says heavily, "bring him inside, I'll see what's wrong with him." He shakes his head again as he walks away and enters his shop.

Russ's shop consists of a main desk with a telephone and cash register, across from which stands a table with a coffee maker, Styrofoam cups, and powdered creamer. Two vinyl chairs sit by a coffee table with magazines on it. A door stands open to the workroom. "Bring him back here," Russ says. Carrying Yang over my shoulder, I follow him into the back room.

The workspace is full of body parts, switch boards, cables, and tools. Along the wall hang disjointed arms, a couple of knees, legs of different sizes, and the head of a young girl, about seventeen, with long red hair. There's a worktable cluttered with patches of skin and a Pyrex box full of female hands. I notice that all the skin tones are Caucasian.

In the middle of the room is an old massage table streaked with grease. Probably something Russ got from Stacey's Seconds. "Go 'head and lay him down there," Russ says. I lay Yang down on his stomach, and position his head in the small circular face rest at the top of the table.

"I don't know what happened to him," I say. "He's always been fine, then this morning he started malfunctioning. He was bending over from the waist again and again." Russ doesn't say anything. "I'm wondering if it might be a problem with his hard drive," I say, feeling like an idiot. I've got no clue what's wrong with him; it's just something George mentioned I should check out. I should have gone to Quick Fix. The young techies there, with their polished manners, always make me feel more at ease. Russ still hasn't spoken. He takes a mallet from the wall and a Phillips head screwdriver. "Do you think it's fixable?" I ask.

"We'll see. I don't work on imports," he says, meeting my eyes for the first time since I've arrived, "but, since you know George, I'll open him up and take a look. Go 'head and take a seat out there."

"How long do you think it'll take?"

"Won't know till I get him opened up," Russ says, wiping his hands on his jeans.

"Okay," I say meekly, and leave Yang in Russ's hands.

In the waiting room I pour myself a cup of coffee and stir in some creamer. I set my cup on the coffee table and look though the magazines. There's *Guns & Ammo, Tech Repair, Big Brothers & Sisters Digest*—I put the magazines back down glumly. The wall behind the desk is cluttered with photos of Russ and his kids, all of whom look exactly like him. There are a couple autographed dollar bills, and, buried among these, a small sign with an American flag on it and the message THERE AIN'T NO YELLOW IN THE RED, WHITE, AND BLUE.

"Pssh," I say instinctually, letting out an annoyed breath of air. This is the kind of crap that came out during the invasion of North Korea, back when the nation changed the color of its ribbons to blue. Ann Arbor's a progressive city, but even there, when Kyra and I would go out with Yang and Mika in public, there were many who avoided eye contact. Stop the War activists weren't any different. It was that first Christmas, as Kyra, Yang, Mika, and I were at the airport being individually searched, that I realized Chinese, Japanese, South Korean, didn't matter anymore; they'd all become threats in the eyes of Americans. I decide not to sit here looking at Russ's racist propaganda, and leave to check out the bear traps at Stacie's.

*

"He's dead," Russ tells me. "I can replace his insides, more or less build him back from scratch, but that's gonna cost you about as much as a used one."

I stand looking at Yang, who's lying on the massage table with a tangle of red and green wires protruding from his back. Even though his skin has lost its vibrant color it still looks soft, like when he first came to our home. "Isn't there anything else you can do?"

"His voice box and language system are still running. If you want, I'll take it out for you. Cost you sixty bucks." Russ is wiping his hands on a rag, avoiding my eyes. I think of the sign hanging in the other room. Sure, I think, I can just imagine the pleasure Russ will take in cutting up Yang.

"No, that's all right. I'll just take him home. What do I owe you?"

"Nothing," Russ says. I look up at him. "You know George," he says as explanation. "Besides, I can't fix him for you."

On the ride home, I call Kyra. She picks up on the second ring.

"Hello?"

"Hey, it's me." My voice is ragged.

"Are you okay?"

"Yeah," I say, then add, "Actually, no."

"What's the matter? How's Yang?"

"I don't know. The tech I took him to says he's dead, but I don't believe him—the guy has a thing against Asians.

I'm thinking about taking Yang over to Quick Fix." There's silence on the other end of the line. "How's Mika?" I ask.

"She's good. She's watching a movie right now . . . Dead?" she asks. "Are you positive?"

"No, I'm not sure. I don't know. I'm not ready to give up on him yet. Look," I say, glancing at the dash clock, "it's only three. I'm gonna suck it up and take him to Quick Fix. I'm sure if I drop enough cash they can do something."

"What will we do if he's dead?" Kyra asks. "I've got work on Monday."

"We'll figure it out," I say. "Let's just wait until I get a second opinion."

Kyra tells me she loves me, and I return my love, and we hang up. It's as my Bluetooth goes dead that I feel the tears coming. I remember last fall when Kyra was watching Mika. I was in the garage taking down the rake when, from behind me, I heard Yang. He stood awkwardly in the doorway as though, while Mika was being taken care of, he was uncertain what to do. "Can I help you," he asked.

On that chilly late afternoon, with the red and orange leaves falling around us—me in my vest, and Yang in the black suit he came with—Yang and I quietly raked leaves into large piles on the flat earth until the backyard looked like a village of leaf huts. Then Yang held the bag open, I scooped the piles in, and we carried them to the curb.

"You want a beer?" I asked, wiping the sweat from my forehead.

"Okay," Yang said. I went inside and got two cold ones from the fridge, and we sat together there on the splintering cedar of the back deck, watching the sun fall behind the trees and the first stars blink to life above us.

"Can't beat a cold beer," I said, taking a swig.

"Yes," Yang said. He followed my lead and took a long drink. I could hear the liquid sloshing down into his stomach canister.

"This is what men do for the family," I said, gesturing with my beer to the leafless yard. Without realizing it, I had slipped into thinking of Yang as my son, imagining that one day he'd be raking leaves for his own wife and children. It occurred to me then that Yang's time with us was limited. Eventually he'd probably be shut down and stored in the basement—an antique that Mika would have no use for when she had children of her own. At that moment I wanted to put my arm around Yang. Instead I said, "I'm glad you came out and worked with me."

"Me too," Yang said, and took another sip of his beer, looking exactly like me in the way he brought the bottle to his lips.

*

The kid at Quick Fix makes me feel much more at ease than Russ. He's wearing a bright red vest with a clean white shirt under it, and a nametag that reads HI, I'M RONNIE! The kid's probably not even twenty-one. He's friendly though, and when I tell him about Yang, he says, "Whoa, that's no good," which is at least a bit sympathetic. He tells me they're backed-up for an hour. So much for quick, I think. I put Yang on the counter and give my name. "We'll page you once he's ready," Ronnie says.

I spend the time wandering the store. They've got a demo station of Championship Boxing, so I put on the jacket and glasses and take on a guy named Vance, who's playing in California. I can't figure out how to dodge or block, though, and when I throw out my hand, my guy on the screen just wipes his nose with his glove. Vance beats the shit out of me, so I put the glasses and vest back on the rack, and go look at other equipment. I'm playing with one of the new ThoughtPhones when I hear my name paged over the loudspeaker, so I head back to the Repair counter.

"Fried," the kid tells me. "Honestly, it's probably good he bit it. He's a really outdated model." Ronnie is rocking back and forth on his heels as though impatient to get on to his next job.

"Isn't there anything you can do?" I ask. "He's my daughter's Big Brother."

"The language system is fully functional. If you want, I can separate the head for you."

"*Are you kidding?* I'm not giving my daughter her Brother's head to play with."

"Oh," the kid says. "Well, um, we could remove the voice box. He can still talk to her, there just won't be any face attached. If you want, we can recycle the body and give you twenty dollars off any digital camera."

"How much is all this going to cost?"

"It's ninety-five for the check-up, and voice box removal will be another hundred and fifty. You're probably looking at about three hundred after labor and taxes."

I think about taking it back to Russ, but there's no way. When he'd told me Yang was beyond saving, I'd given him a look of distrust that anyone could read loud and clear. "Go ahead and remove the voice box," I say, "but no recycling. I want to keep the body."

*

George is outside throwing a football around with his identical twins when I pull in. He raises his hand to his kids to stop them from throwing the ball, and comes over to the low hedge that separates our driveways. "Hey, how'd it go with Russ?" he asks as I get out of the car.

"Not good." I tell him about Yang, getting a second opinion, how I've got his voice box in the backseat, his body in a large Quick Fix bag in the trunk. I tell him all this with as little emotion as possible. "What can you expect from electronics?" I say, attempting to appear nonchalant.

"Man, I'm really sorry for you," he says, his voice quieter than I've ever heard it. "Yang was a good kid. I remember the day he came over to help Dana carry in the groceries. The kids still talk about that fortune-telling thing he showed them with the sticks."

"Yeah," I say, looking at the bushes. I can feel the tears starting again. "Anyhow, it's no big deal. Don't let me keep you from your game. We'll figure it out." Which is a complete lie. I have no clue how we're going to figure anything out. We needed Yang, and there's no way we can afford another model.

"Hey, listen," George says. "If you guys need help, let us know. You know, if you need a day sitter or something. I'll talk to Dana—I'm sure she'd be up for taking Mika." George reaches out across the hedge, his large hand coming straight at me. For a moment I flash back to Championship Boxing and think he's going to hit me. Instead he pats me on the shoulder. "I'm really sorry, Jim," he says.

*

That night, I lie with Mika in bed and read her *Goodnight Moon*. It's the first time I've read to her in months. The last time was when we visited Kyra's folks and had to shut Yang down for the weekend. Mika's asleep by the time I reach the last page. I give her a kiss on her head and turn out the lights. Kyra's in bed reading.

"I guess I'm gonna start digging now," I say.

"Come here," she says, putting her book down. I cross the room and lie across our bed, my head on her belly.

"Do you miss him too?" I ask.

"Mm-hm," she says. She puts her hand on my head and runs her fingers through my hair. "I think saying goodbye tomorrow is a good idea. Are you sure it's okay to have him buried out there?"

"Yeah. There's no organic matter in him. The guys at Quick Fix dumped his stomach canister." I look up at our ceiling, the way our lamp casts a circle of light and then a dark shadow. "I don't know how we're going to make it without him."

"Shhh." Kyra strokes my hair. "We'll figure it out. I spoke with Tina Matthews after you called me today. You remember her daughter, Lauren?"

"The clone?"

"Yes. She's home this semester; college wasn't working for her. Tina said Lauren could watch Mika if we need her to."

I turn to face Kyra. "I thought we didn't want Mika raised by a clone."

"We're doing what we have to do. Besides, Lauren is a nice girl."

"She's got that glassy-eyed apathetic look. She's exactly like her mother," I say. Kyra doesn't say anything. She knows I'm being irrational, and so do I. I sigh. "I just really hoped we could keep clones out of our lives."

"For how long? Your brother and Margaret are planning on cloning this summer. You're going to be an uncle soon enough."

"Yeah," I say quietly.

Ever since I was handed Yang's voice box, time has slowed down. The light of the setting sun had stretched across the wood floors of our home for what seemed an eternity. Sounds have become crisper as well, as though, until now, I'd been living with earplugs. I think about the way Mika's eyelids fluttered as she slept, the feel of George's hand against my arm. I sit up, turn towards Kyra, and kiss her. The softness of her lips makes me remember the first time we kissed. Kyra squeezes my hand. "You better start digging, so I can comfort you tonight," she says. I smile and ease myself off of the bed. "Don't worry," Kyra says, "It'll be a good funeral."

In the hallway, on my way towards the staircase, the cracked door of Yang's room stops me. Instead of going down, I walk across the carpeting to the doorway, push it open, and flick on the light switch. There's his bed, perfectly made with the corners tucked in, a writing desk, a heavy oak dresser, and a closet full of black suits. On the wall is a poster of China that Big Brothers&Sisters Inc. sent us and a pennant from the Tigers game I took Yang to. There's little in the minimalism of his décor to remind me of him. There is, however, a baseball glove on the shelf by his bed. This was a present Yang bought for himself with the small allowance we provided him. We were at Toys R Us when Yang placed the glove in the shopping cart. We didn't ask him about it, and he didn't mention why he was buying it. When he came home, he put it on the shelf near his Tigers pennant, and there it sat untouched.

Along the windowsill, Yang's collection of dead moths and butterflies look as though they're ready to take flight. He collected them from beneath our bug-zapper during the summer, and placed their powdery bodies by the window. I walk over and examine the collection. There's the great winged Luna Moth, with its two mock eyes staring at me, the mosaic of Monarchs' wings, and a collection of smaller non-descript brown and silvery gray moths. Kyra once asked him about his insects. Yang's face illuminated momentarily, the lights beneath his cheeks burning extra brightly, and he'd said, "They're very beautiful, don't you think?" Then, as though suddenly embarrassed, he segued to a Fun Fact regarding the brush-footed butterfly of China.

What arrests me, though, are the objects on his writing desk. Small matchboxes are stacked in a pile on the center of the table, the matchsticks spread across the expanse like tiny logs. In a corner is an orange-capped bottle of Elmer's that I recognize as the one from my toolbox. What was Yang up to? A log cabin? A city of small wooden men and women? Maybe this was Yang's attempt at art—one that, unlike the calligraphy he was programmed to know, was entirely his own. Tomorrow I'll bag his suits, donate them to the Goodwill, and throw out the Big Brothers & Sisters poster, but these matchboxes, the butterflies, and the baseball glove, I'll save. They're the only traces of the boy Yang might have been.

*

The funeral goes well. It's a beautiful October day, the sky thin and blue, and the sun lights up the trees, bringing out the ochre and amber of the season. I imagine what we must look like to the neighbors. A bunch of kooks, burying their electronic equipment like Pagans. I don't care. When I think about Yang being ripped apart in a recycling plant, or stuffing him into our plastic garbage can and setting him out with the trash, I know this is the right decision. Standing together as a family, in the corner of our backyard, I say a couple of parting words. I thank Yang for all the joy he brought to our lives. Then Mika and Kyra say goodbye.

When it's all over we go back inside to have breakfast. We're eating our cereal when the doorbell rings. I get up and answer it. On our doorstep is a glass vase filled with orchids and white lilies. A small card is attached. I kneel down and open it. *Didn't want to disturb you guys. Just wanted to give you these. We're all very sorry for your loss—*

George, Dana, and the twins. Amazing, I think. This from a guy who paints his face for Super Bowl games.

"Hey, look what we got," I say, carrying the flowers into the kitchen. "They're from George."

"They're beautiful," Kyra says. "Come, Mika, let's go put those in the living room by your brother's picture." Kyra helps Mika out of her chair, and we walk into the other room together.

It was Kyra's idea to put the voice box behind the photograph. The photo is a picture from our trip to China last summer. In it, Mika and Yang are playing at the gate of a park. Mika stands at the port, holding the two large iron gates together. From the other side, Yang looks through the hole of the gates at the camera. His head is slightly cocked, as though wondering who we all are. He has a placid non-smile/non-frown, the expression we came to identify as Yang at his happiest.

"You can talk to him," I say to Mika as I place the flowers next to the photograph.

"Goodbye, Yang," Mika says.

"Goodbye?" the voice box asks. "But, little sister, where are we going?"

Mika smiles at the sound of her Big Brother's voice, and looks up at me for instruction. It's an awkward moment. I'm not about to tell Yang that the rest of him is buried in the backyard.

"Nowhere," I answer. "We're all here together."

There's a pause as though Yang's thinking about something. Then, quietly, he asks, "Did you know over two million workers died during the building of the Great Wall of China?" Kyra and I exchange a look regarding the odd serendipity of this Fun Fact, but neither of us says anything. Then Yang's voice starts up again. "The Great Wall is over ten thousand li long. A li is a standardized Chinese unit of measurement that is equivalent to one thousand six hundred and forty feet."

"Wow, that's amazing," Kyra says, and I stand next to her, looking at the flowers George sent, acknowledging how little I truly know about this world.

Ω

Settling Gwendolyn

by Maria Munro-Schuster

All along it was the mystics who sensed it, but it was the scientific community who, after great to-do, were able to produce the almighty evidence. It was the art-science, right brain-left brain, secular-religious way of perceiving the world people had been waiting for. God and the Universe all at once. With the evidence came change, and it was swift. Most can't remember anymore what life was like before Settling. Not everyone has put their faith in this golden age—making the job of Settler one wrought with bothersome obstacles.

I, of course, was a natural choice by the Selection of Official Settlers Committee. I was one of the educated ones—many psychics aren't. A degree in architectural psychology hangs on the wall right behind me. And I've always had this natural connection with structures. As my mother always said, "Homes are not just protection. They are a statement."

Let me tell you about Glimakra House and Gwendolyn Verges, a perfect example of a non-believer converted. She had been house hunting in Atlanta for about six months when she came to me quite hesitantly. Transition was written all over her face. I liked her, she seemed to care about houses in the way that people paint their exterior Gratifying Guava just to feel something when they pull into the driveway. She was just the type of young woman who needed my services.

House care history indicated that she routinely polished the hickory flooring and spent time reading romance novels in the house's uppermost eaves. Her own hand-sketched crayon scribbles hung where people would see them. Knobby brass faucets in the half bath were original. She wouldn't dare paint her exposed brick white, as one interior designer friend told her she should, "to be up with the times."

Why would a person want to leave such an enchanting space, one might wonder? Ms. Verges let go of her structure as people must the ones they love most. And she started having dreams.

Mainstream schools of psychology suggest dreams involving houses or buildings are typically associated with a need for exploring one's internal workings—the state of the house says something about our own state, which we are often unwilling to accept. Those dreams in which you find yourself lost in a mansion—the ones with endless hallways of oriental rugs, and foreboding bare-breasted marble statues, where the ceilings with their gilded chandeliers loom beyond our reach, suggest growth is needed; while yards, brimming with primroses, clipped hedges and neat rows of box vegetable gardens, indicate the ability to organize one's outward appearances, namely that of work and social life. The dreams you want to watch out for are the ones relentlessly repeated. In her dreams, Ms. Verges kept finding herself scaling ladders and crossing beams in a high-ceilinged barn-like structure, roasting large legs of lamb in a stone hearth and employing rustic wooden outhouses—things not done in Atlanta.

This is the point in the Process when I invite a potential client to sit down with me. Over peppermint tea with a splash of milk—my mother's preferred bedtime remedy—I have them close their eyes and meticulously walk me through their dream. Gwendolyn, I noted, liked her tea extra milky.

"I always have to push really hard to get the door open. It's heavy. Like maybe I'm not supposed to go in."

"Oh, you are dear. Please continue."

"It's a grainy, pleasant tone of solid wood."

I hold up a board of wood grain swatches. "Point to the closest match."

She chooses one and continues on. "Oh, the smell in the air is heavenly." Her lashes drape heavily on her cheeks. "The hallway leads straight to a light filled kitchen. There's someone . . ."

"That's enough. Could you back up to the hallway and be a bit more specific? Then let's talk doorknobs."

The initial dream walkthrough may occur ten or more times; in certain cases, I have had to continue sessions another day if the person is having difficulty getting the details straight. They go home and come back when they have had the dream again. It is essential that they have the dream absolutely correct. Accuracy is pertinent because in precise house matches, someone will most likely become homeless.

The search for the house-human match can take years if not carefully executed. And it can be a costly endeavor if we do not have full cooperation. We do take into consideration an individual's financial state and occupation because we feel that everyone has the right to Settle. Ms. Verges shared that she started saving as soon as she had her first repeated house dream four years ago. If the house is a match though, it is the rightful dreamer's at no costs other than those incurred for my services; we believe it is not the owner who wants the house really, but more-so the house the owner. Homes need to be Settled. Once a person makes the decision to pursue my services they are choosing a home in which they will spend the rest of their life.

Every client has quirks, making the Process an arduous task. For Ms. Verges, it was her failure to disclose all the details necessary. Her dream descriptions had allowed me to reach a point in which I had sketched out her house, down to the last exposed nail. While my sketches are rendered in the traditional, hand-crafted sense, unfortunately, these days Settlers are expected to employ the use of technology when locating the Home. Our search engines dig into a data-base of billions of homes world-wide: scratchy, yellow-stranded grass huts, spindly tree houses, stone-walled villas, underground eco lodges, brightly colored canvas teepees, high-ceilinged one room flats, Puglian breast-shaped Trulli. In this case, there should have been no problem loading the dimensions in the program and arriving at a manageable list of potential matches. Except that she kept changing one small detail at a time.

"Oh, my, I think I was wrong again. Last night I had the dream, and it wasn't an exposed loft, it was an attic space."

"I'm so sorry. It was a hinged, not sliding front door."

"Did I say apricot last time? I meant honeysuckle trim above the velvet-striped wallpaper."

I finally had to ask.

"Ms. Verges, is there some reason you do not want to leave the structure you are currently in?"

She looks up from digging in the sugar pot on my desk, that late August afternoon, Gwendolyn in her vintage blue linen summer dress that reminds me of a certain finely crafted lakeside home in Maine, and hastily dumps a large spoonful into her porcelain cup. She is thirty-five, financially secure, with no immediate family in Atlanta. She is also blushing.

"No, of course I want to leave home."

I should have known.

"I didn't say Home, Ms. Verges. Once you have made the choice to follow your dream, you need to refer to your prior living situation as a structure," I stress, tapping on the copy of Settling for Life: A Handbook, resting on my desk, where it is in bold italics on page two. "As you should know, the Home is sacred. It is connecting with you and you show your future home no respect by discarding it in place of your old structure. Now fess up, what is holding you to your structure?"

She sips her sugary tea and coughs.

"I don't know!" she whimpers.

I cringe, not wanting to prompt a sob session. I had other clients to see, and the smell of tears is enough for most of them to find some reason to do the same. I hand her one of the freshly pressed linen hankies from my bottom drawer that I keep prepared for these situations. Talk of homes and structures tends to be an emotional occasion for most. I had forty-five year old Mr. Dryer in my office last week who stubbornly claimed he had a cold and that he was not sniffling because he was leaving his childhood structure for the first time.

Wiping my own brow, I open a black leather binder from my filing cabinet and glance at the list of symptoms in cases of structure attachment.

1. Fear of losing a structure associated with the loss of loved one.

Deep, quiet sobs; hollow eyes; lack of sleep

2. Fear of becoming homeless.

Need to lock oneself in structures and Home; hoarding of objects; finds comfort in soft objects (See "Pillow Test," p. 6-7)

3. Fear of it not being the right Home.

Extreme skepticism of the Process; tendency to spot real-estate publications in obscure locations and view with intense pleasure

4. Fear of letting go of a love in the same location as the structure.

Denial of fear; excessive whimpering

5. Fear of placing unnecessary value on Home.

Finds humor in all associated with the Process; leaves generous tips after sessions (usually in odd, difficult to locate places); suggests ludicrous notions such as living in less suitable homes, i.e. caves, boxes, blow-up play structures (castles), etc.

6. Fear of losing the smell associated with the structure.

Attempts inconspicuous pass of the fingertips to the nasal area after touching things

Well, she certainly seems to be hoarding that sugar pot, I notice, glancing up from the document—she has taken over the pot as her personal Zen garden, using the spoon to rake swirls around the sugar clump rocks. So as not to disturb her, I quietly remove myself from my chair and walk over to the cabinet on the back wall. Retrieving what I am after, I return to my client.

"Ms. Verges, would you like to hold this pillow while we continue?" I say, dangling a plump, cream-colored feather down in front of her.

She stares at it distantly with a slight pout on her face, as if she were five years old and I had just suggested she go to bed when it was still light out. She shakes her head and returns to drawing in the sands of the sugar pot.

Continuing my analysis of her as I return to my chair, I feel I can rule out a number two. She wasn't deeply unhappy, just wistful. And she sighed constantly, just as a bored person yawns.

She is a funny girl, Gwendolyn. She often appears to be on the verge of saying something and then stops herself. She has a nervous habit of puffing up her cheeks like a balloon and when she thinks no one is looking, takes her finger to it, as if a needle, and pops it. Her right bottom lip has become dry and bloody from chewing on it when she has to think about difficult things. I find these things all quite odd, but irresistible—possibly because she is so unaffected by the world and its constraints.

She takes a finger to her nose. I wait. She scratches the end of it with her pinky before pushing up her glasses. No, it wasn't the Maine lakeside, she was more of a Prince Edward cottage—a seaside view—porches embracing the stately lady from all sides, sheets on the breeze in the yard, a gate. I shiver with delight.

"Are we going to continue?" she says looking up at me almost impatiently, "I promise I am fine and as ready as ever to do this." She straightens up in her chair and leans forward with renewed interest.

Check skepticism off the list. She is as eager as anyone. Or, at least, she says she is. Humor was not her forte. Tipping certainly wasn't in her nature or wallet.

"Ms. Verges, who, may I ask, are you in love with?"

She appears as shocked as I am by the charge and flings her sugar spoon out of the pot, sending fine crystals in a scatter across my desk. I dab my pursed lips.

Failure to disclose a relationship of significance results in a misdirected Process. Home and dreamer are severed, and most times the Process is null and void.

I slide a notepad and pen across the desk.

"Give me a name and an address."

I had dealt with love many times before in this business and am well aware that it takes much cajoling and jiggering, but in most cases a sensible resolution is reached after a calm intervention with the individual not in the Process. Individuals in the Process rarely think rationally. And who would let a loved one give up on the once in a lifetime opportunity of Settling?

Two-twelve Windemere Drive comes into view just as the sun begins to stretch lazily through the trees on a Tuesday afternoon in the eastern Atlanta suburb. Putting my car into park, I take a moment to survey the form before me.

The structure is quirky—probably just like him. Faded, slouching, forlorn . . . I jot down quickly on my notepad. Something depressing about the place . . . But at second glance, I can't help noticing something else.

Nestled away from the street, shrouded by the encroaching laurel branches, the two story structure could be pulled straight from the pages of classic Hans Christen Anderson. The arched stonework entryway, mossy and worn, rests atop a stacked handcrafted stairway. A wrought iron lantern dangles just above, providing a soft yellow welcoming glow as the early evening approaches. Antique wooden beams crisscross under the gently bowed eaves, forming a canopy above the wisteria-fringed balcony. Windows peek out from the graying structure, providing sweeping views of the gently wild gardens below. A nest of wood and stone, the structure is a breath of its surroundings, a vision of a time and place when dreams were only a blueprint, a muse for what the mind already knew to be possible. A structure that is actually charming.

I slam my car door shut and climb what I sense is a potentially decaying laurel staircase to the dreadfully pretentious solid laurel and iron flanked doorway. I pause before the entrance, my hand delicately tracing the ornamental swirls etched deep into the wood. I knock, waiting far too long, and then listen to the sound of an elaborate unlatching process, before the door swings open and I am standing face to face with Mr. Peder Jacobs.

I do not care for Mr. Jacobs. You see, he is not the type of man who knows how to tend to a home. Crumbs dangle precariously from his stubble-lined mouth, most likely from a day-old-bread-and-standard-salty-lunchmeat sandwich. His tie, perhaps once a solid bright blue but now faded, is loosened and pushed to the side. His demeanor was young, and yet, his face was starting to give in to time. Somewhat like his structure.

"Please do come in, Ms. Pennmore. I hope you don't mind—the place is a bit of a mess. Been baking this morning and I don't keep things in the bowl very well, if you know what I mean. Would you care for a hot blueberry scone and some tea?" he says, wiping his doughy hands on a perfectly clean towel.

I still do not care for Mr. Jacobs.

"Yes, that would be delightful." She must have told him to prepare in this manner, I assume. Gwen is ever so thoughtful.

Following him into the dimly lit kitchen area I notice that every nook and cranny is filled with some odd and novel artifact. A miniature Dutch windmill gently whirls on a bookshelf. Ceramic vases sprawling with garden iris, hydrangea and lilies enhance every table. Sketched pictures of birds and scientific plant illustrations adorn the walls. An old glass milk bottle holds blue marbles. Quite meticulously, the space is a study in medieval architecture. The walls are covered with rough-cut limestone. Arches fall gracefully over each opening. Dark, chiseled beams exposed above it all. The wood burning stove resides in a deep-set grotto, bordered by rough Gaudian stone mosaic. Lit candles rest on wrought iron wall sconces, while windows and modern electric light fixtures provided the majority of the light.

He pulls out an well-worn antique wooden chair at the table and motions for me to sit. While looking at him my mind trails back to that Detroit Steampunk flat I assisted in Settling two years before—a museum of fantastical trinkets, inventive in how it attempted to make new of the old, but so makeshift. And in the end, unreliable. Clutter for my seaside cottage in the blue linen dress.

"So you are a . . ." I begin, gaining control of my curious glances. I notice antlers above my head. A bicycle floats on wires just to the right of them.

"Scientist."

"Ah, a scientist who also has an interest in baking and . . . whimsical architecture?"

It is all too good to be true.

"Well, the first one's my mother's influence and the second is just a different manifestation of daily work. I'm a physicist and I appreciate the physics of my surroundings, including my home."

"Excuse me, your what?"

"What is it you came for again, Ms. Pennmore?" He asks, setting a cup of steaming tea in front of me. His dark eyes are warm, but noticeably flustered by my presence. He wipes a few beads of sweat from his brow, flecking dough into his grey specked hair.

"As you may know, I am assisting a Ms. Gwendolyn Verges in the matter of Settling. I am here to collect as much information on your association with her as possible, so that we can see that she finalizes her dream. Right now, you are the only thing stopping her from realizing it."

He stops, tea kettle in mid-pour.

"I am?" He looks happily surprised. "I mean, I am?" he says, attempting to switch to a more concerned mannerism.

However concerned he attempts to appear, he looks positively jovial as he begins to pace the room. His realization will most likely cause an unnecessary delay in my task. I sigh, wearily.

"I have been wondering for some time now. I knew that she was in the Process and I had begun to assume that I had lost her," he says throwing his hands up.

"Tell me, Mr. Jacobs," I say, as he looks at me uneasily, "have you had any dreams?"

"Sure, like all sentient beings, I dream. I have dreams about Gwendolyn if that's what you're after. I dream of her day and night. She doesn't know how much because I haven't told her. You see," he says pulling up a chair next to me, smelling just as the Steampunk flat did, like useless creativity, like dust and machines toiled over, "we met in a peach orchard. I was there picking peaches, as I normally would each summer, and I set my full baskets at the bottom of the tree before I would climb back up again. When I came down each time I would swear I had picked more peaches than what was presently there. Soon whole baskets were empty. I decided to set a trap. I climbed high up into the tree, camouflaged by leaves and waited to trap my thief with a basket. When my thief finally came back for more loot, I was unable to drop the basket. She was lovely and strange with her dark hair, freckled skin and bare feet."

I avoid meeting his far-off gaze just by a few inches—I do not want him thinking I am about to give in to his story-teller's rhetoric. He grins like a child.

"She giggled and I could hear the whispers of a nearby friend provoking her. I stayed up in that tree for a long time, continuing to play their game, watching her tiptoe up and grab a peach. Until she didn't come anymore. Luckily, the manager of the orchard knew of my darling thief when I described her. He said she came every now and then, and she would surely come back. So I returned to that orchard every day, missing weeks of work. My co-workers thought I was crazy. The orchard owner thought I was crazy. Even though I had a truckload of peaches in my pantry, I didn't think I was crazy. In the evenings, I would put my energy into this place, in the hope that someday she would see it and fall in love with it. And maybe me."

"So, did she?" I stammer, feeling utterly betrayed by my faithful cottage. She omitted a direct threat to the process—a lover.

"No, I mean, yes. We have met, yes, many times, but she has not seen my, uh, place of residence yet," he declares. "She had started this process with you, and she, being a girl who steals peaches, but who does not break the rules of the Process, has not come here." He looks down at his hands, as if they were to blame.

It brings a smile to my face. I know his type.

"You don't believe in the Process, do you Mr. Jacobs?"

"I don't believe in it because it has left so many homeless. So many on the streets because of dreams. Out of fear, I began to build my own house, and through the process, I lost my fear," he says, standing up quickly from his seat.

"But what if someone dreams of what you have built?"

"Let them dream. I doubt anyone could dream up this place. That's why I keep adding to it. Each day a new detail."

*

When a person is having difficulty with the Process of Settling it is key that the expert Settler keep the more delicate details to a minimum. In Gwendolyn Verges' fragile state, it was of the utmost importance that I share with her what I ultimately believed to be Mr. Jacob's most earnest intentions in the matter.

After a few hours tweaking some of the house drawings and scouring the database, I arrived at something that seemed more appropriate for Gwen. Not even she knew what she wanted anymore, poor girl, and a slightly altered depiction merely enhanced her original image. Precision is sometimes overrated, an expert Settler once told me—you just need to know when to be Michelangelo and when Picasso will do.

With as much melancholy as I can muster, I take her hand to give her the news. Her hand is slightly sticky and smells of peach juice.

"After paying Mr. Jacobs a visit, and with my experience and expertise in these matters, I have come to conclude that Mr. Jacobs has not had the same dream as you, my dear."

She sinks down into her seat and fat tears begin to fall onto her lap one by one. I was expecting this. I yank open the drawer of hankies and offer one to her. She ignores it—deciding instead to soak my hand-stitched black leather Jacobsen egg chair (I trust only an architect to design where I place my hind end).

Trying to impart some cheer to the girl, the one who was so close to what some girls only dream of, I offer, "Mr.

Jacobs and I came to the conclusion that it is best that you finalize the

Process and get Settled in life. Your Home is waiting for you," I stress, as I again hold up the photograph I have printed of her Home in the Swedish countryside, just a mile from a quaint village brimming with picturesque artisanal cheese and pastry shops.

She looks past it to me. "You mean his home is not my home? How can that be? I was almost sure it would be," she insists, her wide eyes pleading with mine. "I believed in our love so much. I thought doing this would only make it stronger."

"Even if what wasn't, was, his home is not good enough for you," I say, concentrating on folding the handkerchief and placing it, unused, back in the drawer. "You deserve the one that has been waiting for you."

*

That afternoon I got a call from Mr. Jacobs. It had been a long morning and I was not in the mood for bargaining. The Process was closed, but I listened out of courtesy. Gwendolyn was already safely at her structure, filling boxes with all of her crayon art.

"This is ludicrous," the conversation begins. "A house is not a person. It doesn't live, breath or have emotions. No blood in its veins. It doesn't love her. I do. So she had dreams, what does that mean? I have dreams all the time that I am operating on myself—that doesn't mean that I should start doing it. Really, Ms. Pennmore, what is this nonsense all about?" He sputters and spits into the phone so much I find myself holding the receiver at a distance. Mr. Jacobs is young and he, like many, has forgotten.

"How many people do you know, Mr. Jacobs, who fall innocently in love, plan their happy future together in their perfect structure, then search for it, with no success? There always has to be compromise. A letting go of something that matters." I place my hand firmly on the copy of Settling resting on the desk before me. "She wants the open floor plan with the large garden, he wants the cozy den and the large garage with the bar. Then slowly, over time, the marriage begins to decay before the caulking in the bathtub begins to peel. With dreams, a person can be sure that they aren't giving up anything; it is left up to the wisdom of the subconscious. Love these days is far too logical. Just because a beautiful girl steals your peaches it does not mean she is the right one for you."

"What is wrong with a little logic every now and then, Ms. Pennmore? My subconscious has dreamt of the girl for sometime. But when my mind first considered Gwen she was different from what I thought I wanted and, in reality, she was better. She was real and unimaginable. Don't you think that from compromise people learn what matters the most, instead of always getting everything they want?"

I sit silently for a moment, letting my hand loosen its grip from the telephone.

"According to our guidelines, Mr. Jacobs, perfect partnerships are arrived at only when both individuals dream of the same house. If one dreams of a house and the other doesn't, then it just isn't meant to be. Gwendolyn's life will be better now."

"I would happily renovate my entire structure to make it hers," he pleads.

"Renovation is not an option," I say as I glance through the most recent Settling guidelines to make sure I have the authorities behind me on this one. "No, Mr. Jacobs, renovation is like plastic surgery . . . in the end the true structure of the place will show through, flaws and all. You can't change how the world sees you with a few staples."

*

Her move-in day was a joyous occasion.

In the early hours of the morning, two hours before her arrival, I made my way to the bustling Glimakra house to document the removal of the Bergman family, a homely clan of five, each toting a box of personals, remainders after the moving truck had left. The youngest girl sat on the stoop of the steps while her parents loaded the last of the bags and boxes into their hatchback.

Breathing deeply of the fresh air, I survey the wet green hills surrounding me; the Swedish countryside is a lovely snapshot of the past Atlanta would never regain. I hope this will never change for Gwen.

"Nathalie!" The mother calls to the girl impatiently.

Nathalie sits in defiance, hugging her stuffed whale, a look of impenetrable indignation on her face. It begins to rain, but she holds fast to her post. I walk up the pathway to Gwen's new home, approaching the girl on the steps.

I bend down to meet her eye level. "Make sure you are a good girl and you listen to your dreams," I coo softly, as I reach out to stroke her light hair. She ducks her head and I pull my hand back to my purse straps.

She looks at me, confused, not understanding a word I said, and runs down the path into the arms of her mother. From the steps, I watch as they drive off to parts un-known—a scene similar to one stamped in my own memory. My mother and I speeding off in the Chevy when I was ten. My father stayed; hiding, I imagined, just behind the closed front door of our home which had just slammed in his face. He had important work to do. That was what he always said. He never did know how to care for a home, my mother said as we drove away.

Gwen's new home is a dream. It is a remodel, an old 18th century farmhouse given new life—just in time for Gwen's. The traditional Swedish rough wood paneled exterior is complimented by sleek walls of window squares. The concrete tiled roof, once giving way to the wooden ceiling beams below, is now held by much safer steel beams. Through the sliding refurbished barn doors, one enters into a world of tranquility with white walls and blond floors. A sturdy bright red brick fireplace stands as heart to the home. And out back, in its place under the birch tree, was her outhouse.

I imagine her here with her newfound friends; glowing face made all plump and happy by the light of the fire in the cozy living room. She might share a few details about her old life, but she would never speak too much about herself.

She is more interested in learning the ways of her new life, like where the women pick the lingonberries for the jams they offer at morning tea. What makes them laugh. Who to speak to in the village about setting up an art cafe—more space for Swedish-inspired crayon scribbles. They might ask her how she came to live in this place, prodding with their smiles: Was she Settled?—and she would modestly mention my name, but not the dream. Gwen knows not to mention it until she hears it from the lips of a possible partner—guidelines, guidelines, I told her before she left—which I do hope works out for her.

*

After arriving home from Sweden and receiving the final payments in the accounts of Ms. Verges' Process, I drove to her old structure to place a "For Sale or Settling" sign in the yard. Gazing upon the Queen Anne's chipped white exterior, I'm reassured in the decision made to leave this structure. It was nice, but too simple for her tastes. Too familiar, like a well-worn stuffed whale. No, for Gwen I saw bigger and better things.

The Process is in some ways like reading palms; I have to adjust at times according to what I can sense the person needs. Even my mother would be proud. She knew what it took to be here. She was there thirty years ago when I was ordained. Women were not even ordained as priests in those days. But Settlers we could be. In silken purple robes, her hand on my right shoulder, I first recited: I believe in the reality of the subconscious, the true living nature of the Home, the lasting foundation which the Home provides for

all of life's endeavors, and the essential journey of the Process. I hum that sweet oath when I feel most conflicted.

*

Shortly after, I pull up to my Mignon—my little darling.
The yard is like a finely groomed French poodle, elaborately
detailed yes, but necessary. I have pulled at its tangled mane
for years and finally, I am satisfied with its outcome.

My abode, however, I have not touched. The plain
white French Colonial attempts to be traditional but fails
on account of its Spanish influenced metalwork gracing the
shutters and the slightly mismatched orange stucco, not
brick, addition from several years back. It has two front
doors, not one. Which results in the all-too-often scenario
of a package being left in the rain, only to be found when it
is too late to salvage the contents.

My eye is drawn to the condensation forming between
the panes of the front window, the one with the seat from
which I view the world. I always feel much better when I
can just get inside. It is one of those places that appears
much larger on the outside than it is on the inside.

I walk through the entryway and see a man sitting in a
deep leather armchair, immersed in The Times. He is the
modernist, sleek, even lines, open. Standing silently in the
entryway, not setting my purse down, I admire his raw edges—the way he has no apprehension at exposing his internal workings. So clean. Not a speck of dust settles on his
soul, my Alan. I wait for him to notice me, just as he always
does. Even when I am at my most invisible, he notices. A
moment later he is peeking around the paper, "You are just

the woman I have been waiting for," he says—a familiar look of mischief and satisfaction from my partner.

"Oh," I feign innocence as I remove my shoes and fall into the chair beside his, so exhausted I don't foresee myself moving from the spot for several hours.

He comes over and stoops to kiss me.

"Mi Amor," he pulls close to me, and begins to loosen my hair and massage my scalp, "I know it is difficult going to work each day, facing clients who are Settling. I look forward to the day when you have your dream of our home."

I smile, nod my head, and close my eyes to rest. I did promise him it would happen eventually. Being a Settler, I had said, we can sense these things.

*

The night came as it always did. The sheets of our bed were as fresh as the ones hung in the yards of country homes. They were optimal for dreaming, as Alan would say, "of far off places." We fell asleep holding hands, as we always did. And I dreamed, just as I always did.

There was a house. The yard is finely groomed, like a French poodle, elaborately detailed, but necessary. The French Colonial attempts to be traditional, but fails . . .

Ω

Sophie Tucker's Dress

by Marjorie Saunders

Harriet packed her husband's lunch, the last she would make, cold meatloaf on rye. One-way tickets, New York to Miami, on the Silver Meteor, lay tucked in her dresser drawer. Gloria, her daughter, still slept.

On the way out, she hugged her neighbor and friend, Doris, who stooped to kiss Gloria before thrusting a package into Harriet's hands. Passing the bank of apartment buzzers, Harriet fixed on the one with her husband's last name, remembering her pride when the super had put it up. She pushed open the front door and hurried toward the 96th Street subway. President Truman had declared a national state of emergency, the paper's headline read, but Harriet had her own imperative.

On the train she read aloud a story about an orphaned boy in a mansion with only animals for companions. Gloria followed along the line with her finger. By New Jersey, they became bored and hungry. Harriet had packed cream cheese and olive sandwiches, hard-boiled eggs and salt in triangles of waxed paper, but they were gone by the afternoon.

"The dining car is now open for the six o'clock dinner seating," the porter announced, a reddened hand on the back of each seat.

"Mommy, can we eat in the train restaurant?" Gloria begged.

Harriet combed her daughter's hair and reached under her plaid gathered skirt to pull her blouse down.

Seated across from a fastidiously dressed older man, Harriet asked if Florida was like the pictures, all beautiful beaches, palm trees and sunsets. In heavily accented English he told them yes indeed. He had real estate investments in the Sunshine State, so sure was he of its potential. Harriet put her hand over her daughter's to stop her from spinning the silver shaker. The man smiled and recommended the lamb chop. It arrived wearing a frilly paper hat accompanied by a dish of mint jelly. When the meal ended, the man stood up and, with a slight bow said that while he had misgivings about being seated with a child, Gloria was a lovely young lady who knew how to handle a knife and fork.

That night, as they sped through the Carolinas, Gloria's head bounced on her mother's lap making it impossible for Harriet to sleep. By dawn, her eyes stung. It had been a mistake, she thought, to wear her best navy suit. She had thought she should look smart for the train, but by the time they reached their destination, she knew she would look crumpled and soiled.

Doris, her neighbor, had an uncle who had given her the name of a residential hotel in Miami Beach, assuring her of its respectability. At first glance it looked promising, the front door etched with a flamingo, but the lobby disappointed, poorly lit with scuffed terrazzo floors in need of a good scrubbing. Not at all what she had expected, but then nothing so far in her life had been. The second floor room contained a narrow bed and folded cot. Harriet opened the jalousies and called to Gloria to look out at the beach and the cobalt blue sky.

"Where will daddy sleep when he comes?" Gloria asked.

"We'll get something larger."

Harriet's body ached, yet that first night in the hotel she laid awake listening to stranger's voices, a radio, "I lay awake nights and ponder world troubles, my answer is always the same . . ." reached her before a door slammed. She remembered the package in brown paper she had stuffed into the outer pocket of her suitcase. She slipped off the string, reused from a bakery box, and felt inside. Money. Ten tens. She wished now she had pushed the package back into Doris's hands, but how was she to know it was cash, cash her friend could ill afford.

In the morning, she forced a smile for Gloria's sake. They put on their bathing suits and the mother and daughter cover-ups she had sewn in anticipation of their new tropical life. The sun stunned her into queasiness, yet she managed to show Gloria how to pack a bucket with moist sand, unmold it and create a fairy circle of pail-shaped mounds. Gloria watched people bob in the surf, hanging close while her mother dozed on a towel. At lunch they walked to a nearby drugstore and ate grilled cheese sandwiches and drank chocolate milk. Men in brightly patterned short-sleeved shirts and women wearing noisy bracelets bought cigarettes, candy and newspapers and left with purpose. Harriet wondered what kind of work they did and why on a weekday they dressed so casually. Maybe, she thought, they wondered about her as well. In the afternoon Gloria napped, while she made lists of her expenses: rent, meals and incidentals.

That afternoon they walked to the market. A boy, high in a palm tree, reached up, picked a coconut, and dropped it where it rolled to a full stop at Harriet's feet. He shimmied down and held it out to her.

"Free," he said.

"What do I do with it?"

"Glad you asked."

He held up his hand traffic cop style stopping two girls biking toward them. He raised the coconut above his head and threw it hard against the pavement signally for Gloria to retrieve it. He smashed it to the sidewalk again and again and again. Gloria threw it once, but it rolled only a few feet. He showed them the crack in the mottled shell and, with a show of grunting, widened it with his hands.

"What happens now?" Gloria asked.

"Come along. I'll show you."

Gloria skipped after him, and Harriet felt she had no choice but to follow.

He led them to a hardware store; the walls piled to the ceiling with boxes. Nails. Screws. Washers. The boy leaned over the counter showing the threadbare seat of his dungarees. "Carlos? Carlos!"

"Be right with you!"

Carlos looked like Dick Tracy, square jaw, irises nearly as black as his pupils.

"Lady needs to crack open her coconut," the boy said.

"Well." Carlos smiled. A gaping hole, missing teeth, marred his looks. "I have something right here that'll do the trick." He reached beneath the counter and, with a flourish, set down a metal ball on four hinged legs the size of a grapefruit. He stepped back as if allowing the contraption room to speak for itself.

"This, young ladies," he said, raised thick brows, "is the answer to that hard to open coconut."

Harriet had been clutching the giant nut to her chest. Now she placed it in Carlos's extended hand. He flipped open the hinged ball, transforming it into two bowls, the nut fitting neatly into the bottom half. Side screws twisted until the nut held firm. He tilted it toward her. Black dots on a hairy shell.

"Looks just like a monkey's face, don't it?"

Gloria nodded.

Carlos pierced the holes with an awl, unscrewed the nut and produced a glass from beneath the counter. He raised and lowered the coconut as if pouring a cocktail allowing a pale milky stream to flow.

"Ah," he said, after taking a sip. "Good for what ails you." He held out the glass and, Harriet, not wanting to be rude, took a taste. Its bluish white hue and its warm temperature unsettled her, like something fresh from an animal.

"Delicious. Thank you."

"And you, little lady? Don't believe I caught the name."

"My name is Gloria."

He held out the glass. Gloria stepped back and shook her head "no."

"Well, you're missing a big treat."

"She's shy," Harriet said.

"No, I'm not," Gloria said.

Carlos closed and opened the now empty hinged ball. "It can also be used for any of your hard to hold while you cut 'em fruits. Cantaloupe, honeydew, casaba, what have you. Invented it myself. Patent pending."

Harriet and Gloria sat on a bench outside the store with a piece of the coconut Carlos had given them. Gloria gnawed the shard of brown shell until it was streaked with translucent stripes on its inside. When they stood up, Carlos came out of the store, as if he had been observing their movements. He held one of his inventions. "Only a few of these left, " he said. "Once they hit the stores, the price will triple."

"Thank you for opening the coconut for us. I will definitely think about buying one." Harriet smoothed the skirt of her dress as she stood up.

"I've heard that before," Carlos said. He leaned over the side of the steps, made a guttural sound, brought up phlegm and spit. Harriet turned from the blob of slime and looked toward her daughter who, thankfully, was busying herself pulling tufts of weed that poked through the sidewalk. She grabbed her hand and hurried her away. Behind her she heard Carlos snort and laugh.

*

The following morning they returned to the beach. An hour after they arrived Harriet noticed a woman nearby reading a book. Her legs were folded to one side and she had the erect spine of a ballerina. Every few minutes she looked up toward the ocean and shaded her eyes. A little boy ran up from the ocean, kept a distance from the woman, rolled himself in the sand, then headed straight back to the water. At lunch the two of them ate sandwiches from a tin box and drank from a thermos; a device Harriet considered dangerous having heard that the glass interior could shatter and be ingested with fatal consequences.

That evening the wind dragged slate gray clouds across the sun. Harriet sat in the chair watching the palms fronds whip like the heads of so many disapproving women. Gloria sat on her cot and cut out paper dolls, whined that she was bored, then fell asleep, the red plastic scissors near her hand.

The room was close with the rain's moist presence. Maybe just this once, Harriet thought, she could leave her daughter alone. Surely if she woke, she would know enough to come downstairs. Harriet tucked cigarettes, lighter and keys into the pocket of her dress just as the rain began pelting the pavement, lifting from it a scent like scorched ironing. Up North when it rained, the air cooled, while here it stirred it like a pot of thick soup.

A woman sat on the porch her back to the doorway, black hair pulled tightly into a chignon. Even without the white turban she had worn on the beach, Harriet recognized her. She drew up a chair and, to avoid staring at the face bent over her sewing, she examined the woman's shoes, open toed sandals the shade of a foundation garment. She lit a cigarette. The woman turned to her. "Oh, she said. "That looks so nice. May I trouble you for just one?"

"Of course." Harriet tapped a cigarette out of the pack.

"I have seen you. With pretty little girl."

"Yes, my daughter, Gloria." Harriet lit the woman's cigarette. "I'm Harriet. "We just moved here."

"My name is Lyuba." The hand she extended had mauve nails with half moons left clear at the base. She took a few puffs on her cigarette and then looked over Harriet's shoulder. "Look, we have a little visitor."

Gloria was standing behind them.

"I have a boy who will play with you tomorrow if you go back to room and get some beauty sleep, Sweetheart."

Gloria tugged at Harriet's arm once, but then, much to her surprise, turned and ran back inside. She stood and watched her daughter scamper up the stairs. "Goodnight, Pumpkin," she called after her. Once she heard the door slam shut, she sat back down.

"And your husband?" Lyuba asked.

Although Harriet had prepared herself for this question, its suddenness stopped her heart. No one had asked it on the train. Or when she checked into the hotel. This was her debut with the story, a different one than she had given Gloria.

"He passed away."

"Oy gutten himmel. A young man."

"Yes. An accident. A truck hit him just as he stepped off the sidewalk. Right in front of our apartment building." Images formed, the small pitiful funeral, Doris's noodle casserole.

"Tsk, tsk, tsk." Lyuba dipped her needle into a peppermint tin scooping up a bead. She secured it with a few deft stitches.

"What are you making?"

"I'm not making. I'm decorating. This one has sequins in front down to here." She caressed herself from breast to waist, with an intimacy surprising to Harriet.

"You must go to a lot of parties," she said.

"Me? No. Some day, yes, but not now, not yet."

"So, why are you decorating the dress?"

"I decorate for dressmakers. I'm saving to move to Broadmoor apartments with Sasha, my boy. This place," she tilted her chin toward the hotel behind them, "isn't really a home."

"I need to save money to move also."

"Can you sew?"

"Yes."

"Well, then. Plenty of work here." Lyuba stabbed two pins into the hem of the dress. "It won't make you rich, maydele, but until you find a man, you won't have to eat dirt."

It seemed that someone, a middleman, Lyuba called him, brought the dresses, and she was paid by the piece. She worked in the lobby during the day, and at night sat on the porch. If "her little man, Sasha" woke, he knew where to find her. One problem, she said, was that the weather made her fingers swell. "But, from where I come from in Ukraine, I should not be one to complain about heat." Her laugh was cut short by a fit of coughing.

A routine developed. The next three mornings, Harriet and Gloria met Lyuba and Sasha at the beach. Sasha played with Gloria, showing her how to make drip castles, canals, and ponds they populated with tiny fish caught at the water's edge. Profoundly grateful her daughter had found such an agreeable playmate; Harriet offered to treat the children to ice cream.

She led them to a stand on Collins Avenue, the main drag, where she had bought herself an occasional coffee. When Lyuba saw where she was headed, she clutched at her arm. Harriet felt the bite of her nails.

"You buy from that goniff?" Lyuba hissed. "He puffs up drink with ice cubes. I want water, I get free."

Lyuba steered them to another stand on a side street where you got "real value for your money."

"Vanilla for you, Sasha," Lyuba ordered. "Why stain good clothes?"

Gloria wanted chocolate.

"She runs you." Lyuba said. And, indeed, Harriet noticed that Sasha, while strong willed with Gloria, acceded to his mother's demands, without question.

When Sasha finished, Lyuba lifted his arm, "Look at this!" she sniffed, displaying the brown streaks to the elbow. "We'll go get clean."

At the hotel Harriet was invited to their room. A corner apartment, a floor above hers, the space was larger and, although furnished with the same rattan furniture and gingko patterned cushions, it had two windows and a tiny strip kitchen. Without being asked, Lyuba volunteered what she paid weekly, only three dollars more than Harriet paid for a much smaller room with no kitchenette. Here was a greenhorn, she thought, who knew better than she how to position herself in a new place. Just last night at the drugstore Gloria had begged for a lamb chop. "Please, mommy, please. Let's pretend we're on the train, ok?" Harriet had ordered it, rationalizing that Gloria never finished her food, and there would be enough for both of them, but that was not the case, and she had slept fitfully, her stomach growling.

"I have something to show you," Lyuba said. She stooped and pulled a large box from beneath her bed, the name of a store in elaborate script on its lavender cover. Inside, peacock blue, emerald green, and ruby red dresses nestled between layers of tissue. Lyuba lifted each dress folding it over her arm, a dozen ghosts doing back bends. Bags of jewel-like beads were tucked in the corners of the box. "Plenty of work to keep us both busy as bees," Lyuba said. She sat down on the bed and patted the spot next to her.

"Lyuba, thank you so much. I can't tell you how much I appreciate your sharing this work with me." She turned to Gloria who was filling in a page of a coloring book with Sasha. "Gloria, time to go."

"Oh, stay. The childrens can have egg sandwich for lunch," Lyuba announced.

"Can I help you?"

"No, you be guest."

When the sandwiches were placed in front of them at the little table, Gloria held half of hers up to her mother.

"No, thank you, Pumpkin," Harriet said.

"Such a generous girl."

Nothing was offered to Harriet and Lyuba ate nothing.

*

The two women became fixtures in the lobby; chairs pulled close, a dress draped across their laps like a shared blanket. Often Lyuba lay down her needle, raised her hands and shook them above her head to relieve the swelling, and Harriet followed suit. They shared stories about their lives or the lives of friends in the places they had left behind. Lyuba told of her beautiful friend in Odessa, Natalya, whose husband threw boiling water on her. "Face look like crumpled washcloth," she said, wrinkling her own as illustration. In another story, a cousin, a sophisticated Muscovite, disappeared on her way to the bank. Lyuba shucked off her thimble and snapped her fingers. "Gone just like that. Of course, I knew she was going to withdraw money from that son of a bitch husband. Maybe kidnapped. Maybe killed." She shrugged.

Harriet yearned to confide her own sorrows, yet the words dissolved on her tongue. Life for her had not been one where husbands hired men to kidnap or kill their wives. They did the damage themselves, incrementally. She spoke of Doris, her childless neighbor and confidante who had been thrilled to entertain Gloria, baking oatmeal cookies or planning outings to the park or the zoo. She had started a letter to her and would finish it that evening.

Dear Doris,

From the outside here everything looks clean and new. But inside it is dirtier and darker. Not like the grime on our windowsills that we used to complain about, but a sour smell that lingers. Everything takes so long to dry and the mildew clings to our clothes.

I have met a foreign woman, a friend, who has given me work, sewing beads on dresses and she has a little boy Gloria's age. You should see how beautifully they play together. Our little Gloria is growing up.

I worry that Frank has come looking for me and that he would bother you. If you need to call the police, do, although we both know how much good they were!

You should never have given me so much money, but you did and I thank you from the bottom of my heart. You knew it would come in handy and it has.

Missing you and hoping this finds you well.

With love,

Harriet

*

In the short few weeks Gloria had become independent, Harriet noticed. She never quarreled with Sasha, her one companion, nor he with her. Residents stopped to chat while the women sewed. Betty, whose husband was a linen supply salesman, pregnant with her first child, was a frequent visitor.

"The day Gloria was born was the happiest one of my whole life," Harriet told her. Gloria hearing her name spoken, left off playing and ran to her mother's side encouraging Harriet's effusiveness. "I cradled your warm little head in the crook of my arm and counted your ten little fingers and toes." She kissed Gloria's damp curls. What she did not talk about was that on the night she went into labor, her husband had been on a two-day bender with his pals. When the nurse asked if he was in the waiting room, she replied that he was ill, and endured the pursed lips and stony silence. Sasha's birth, Lyuba offered, involved hours of torture, no medicine to dull the pain and an indifferent nurse who sat outside her room and read a magazine. Betty stroked her belly in response to both accounts.

There was another guest, an odd little man who always wore a cape. Unlike others, he never stopped, only nodded or offered perfunctory greetings before scurrying away and up the stairs. He was in town, Lyuba explained, to see a famous doctor for a strange malady, a leg that grew from the center of his back. "Not a big leg like ours. Little. But a leg." she said and clucked her tongue, a sound denoting bad luck disproportionately doled out.

One afternoon Lyuba flung the bodice of the dress she was working on onto the floor. Startled Harriet looked up to see a man burst into the lobby. He was handsome with tanned skin and curly blonde hair, and his presence charged the air with a wild current.

"How's my Russian princess?" he asked. She stood on her toes and they hugged.

"My name's Ronald or Ronnie. You can call me anything, just not late for dinner."

"Meet our meal ticket," Lyuba said. She giggled coyly, in a way new to Harriet. "You're your own ticket to a meal, Doll." He flung his arm around her and pulled her close. "The boss took notice of your work. And Sophie Tucker," he paused to look at each of them in turn "will be singing right here on Miami Beach."

"When is this? Lyuba shrieked

"In about . . ." Ronnie raised his eyes as if consulting a calendar on the ceiling," a month or so."

Lyuba clapped and jumped, short small gymnastic leaps.

Sophie Tucker. The Last of the Red Hot Mamas. She made jokes about sex like a man and shook her fat flesh proudly.

Sophie, Ronnie told them, had a particular floor length gown, a shade he referred to as "dubonnet," that she needed for her upcoming show. And, there would be costume changes, many. Others would be eager for the work, but the boss had seen the quality of theirs and insisted they were the ones for the job. The dresses were right outside in the back of his car. They followed him to where they lay slack and sad, it felt to Harriet. Ronnie hoisted and carried them on outstretched arms up the stairs where they rustled before settling down in Lyuba's tiny closet.

A pitcher filled with iced tea was in the refrigerator and Harriet wondered if this was a drink Lyuba made specially since it hadn't been offered the day she had visited. Ronnie took a chair and the two women sat on the edge of the bed leaning toward him.

"I got an interesting job down here," he said, as if one of them had inquired. "Meet a lot of show business people and, you know, they aren't all as stuck-up as you'd think." He held his glass out as if for a toast. "Get someone to watch the kids. I'll take the two of you out."

"I couldn't," Harriet said.

"Why not?" Lyuba asked.

"Gloria. She wouldn't understand."

"You go. She can stay with me and Sasha. I take good care for you."

"No. No. Really."

"Well, that's a damned shame." Ronnie rubbed his hands on his thighs. "If you can't go yourself, I'll place a bet for you. Give me ten bucks and I'll bring you back a hundred."

"He's a lucky guy," Lyuba said, patting his arm. "He won money for me. You have to spend money to get money. This is way in business."

Ronnie winked at her. "Can't argue with your girlfriend here."

Lyuba was smiling and nodding in encouragement.

Harriet opened her bag and took out her wallet. Her bills were folded carefully, first the ones, then the fives. There were two tens. She looked up to see them watching her. She handed a ten to Ronnie.

After he left, Lyuba asked, "Why Harriet, you didn't want to go to the races? He is interested in you."

"He invited us both. What makes you think he wants me alone?"

"There is some things I know," she shrugged; a gesture Harriet recognized indicating no more discussion was necessary. Her eyes dropped to the pocketbook Harriet carried. She stroked it with her flame tipped fingers. "This bag you have is very beautiful."

"Thank you so much. I made this. A friend in New York taught me."

"No! You did this? Very, very magnificent."

"I'm glad you like it."

"You could get lots of money for this kind bag."

"You think so?"

"Absolutely. This is what they call accessory." She took Harriet's bag and put it in the crook of her elbow, tilted her chin up and turned her face towards Harriet. "Wealthy women pay good money for accessory."

"I could easily teach you how to make this," Harriet said. "Maybe Ronnie will know where we can get the form with the clasp. My neighbor, Doris, got them in the garment district. Maybe Sophie Tucker would like one."

Lyuba's laugh this time was a full-throated peal.

That night, when Gloria was asleep, Harriet took out a ball of yarn and a needle. In the bottom of her knitting bag, she found a folded envelope with beads, the wrong color and size, for sure, but as she crocheted, she felt a trill of excitement as the pattern came back to her. It had been a bitter cold winter afternoon in Doris's apartment when she had been taught to crochet. She remembered learning about the flowery scented tea, Jasmine, that was Doris's favorite, her friend's chubby hands around the mug and the hiss of the radiator. Suddenly her husband's face, cheeks flushed with rage as she opened the door to his knocking replaced the softer images. Gloria must be told soon that her father would not be joining them.

*

"This is way we work." Lyuba said. "We must figure what costs us. Yarn, beads, clasps." She was so close; Harriet smelled the spearmint gum on her breath. "How much you think bag like that cost in American stores?"

"I don't know. We could look in the shops."

"Yes, but the fancy shops. Not where poor ladies buy."

"You know better than I," Harriet said and turned her attention to the pink paillettes they were sewing on a satin fitted top.

They boarded the bus marked Miracle Mile, the name itself an omen for impending success. The children loved the sidewalks that Lyuba explained shimmered because mica was mixed into the cement. Only a few people strolled the broad avenue midweek, and Harriet had the odd sensation that this was staged. At any moment dancers would emerge from the shops and burst into song. A window displayed handbags nestled on sandy mounds. Blue scarves floated above. "This is done with invisible wire from ceiling," Lyuba said. "You watch kids while I pretend to be customer."

"You're a witch and you're going to eat me if I don't tell you where the treasure is," Sasha shrieked.

"No, silly, I'm a lady, and I am in trouble. My daddy will save me." Gloria said.

It had been days since Gloria had mentioned her father and now here he was again. Harriet held her breath. Perhaps Lyuba had told Sasha her lie, that Gloria's father was dead, but he said nothing. She had been spared, but the moment served as a warning.

"Just as I thought," Lyuba said, suddenly by Harriet's side. "This bag," she pointed in the window to a beige clutch with wooden handles, "is twenty dollars and ninety-nine cents."

Harriet gasped. "We could make a bag like that for a fraction of the price. But, where would I get the supplies?"

"This is not big problem. Ronnie knows supplier."

Lyuba looped her arm through Harriet's as they strolled pausing before a jewelry display, disembodied gold hands rising from silver waves each draped with a dozen glittering bracelets. A silver dolphin leaped against an electric blue background.

Sasha howled, a high animal shriek. They turned to see his knees pumping and his hands wildly flapping.

"What is this crazy thing?" Lyuba said, grabbing his arm and jerking him to a stop. He fell to the pavement, still screaming. An angry welt rose on his arm.

At a nearby park, they found a fountain. Harriet had a handkerchief that they wet and applied to the swelling. Then they sat on the stone bench waiting for their bus while Sasha, face smeared with dirt and tears, slumped against Gloria and slept. Harriet reached over to smooth the damp hair from his forehead.

That night Gloria had to be reassured that Sasha would not die. "But, how do you know, Mommy?" she asked, and even when Harriet hugged her and told her that bee stings were not fatal, she worried still. "But, you don't know for sure. Do you?" she asked.

Once she was sound asleep, Harriet tucked two cigarettes into her pocket before going down to the porch. Lyuba claimed not to be a smoker, yet she could smoke two of

Harriet's cigarettes each evening. Although they had been together at the drugstore counter when Harriet stocked up, Lyuba never bought her own pack. Something in this small meanness, the pretense of hoarding her cigarettes disturbed Harriet. Uncertain of her motives, she replaced the removed cigarettes, and then guiltily removed them again. She didn't like to think of herself as ungenerous and, for a moment, she thought that maybe in Miami she needed to be.

Lyuba sat in her usual place, the soft slap of waves audible in the distance. Harriet asked about Sasha and was reassured that, after being given an aspirin, he had gone to sleep.

"I lied to you about something," Harriet said, the confession, perhaps, meant to offset her stinginess with the cigarettes.

Lyuba turned, eyebrows raised.

"It would be easier for me if my husband were dead." Her throat tightened. "But, he's alive. I left him to come here. Divorce is easier in Florida, if I ever try to get one. I need to find the right way to tell Gloria her father won't be coming. I haven't yet."

Lyuba waved her hand in front of her face as if swatting away a fly. "This happens lots of times with Russian men," she sighed. "They come here, think they are big shots and good-bye family. Sasha has been used long time to no daddy."

"Is that what happened with your husband?"

"I was first one out the door. I don't give bastard chance."

"In Russia?"

"Long story." Lyuba's laugh was harsh and, rather than elaborate, she drew in the last smoke of her cigarette and then fiercely tamped it out under her shoe.

"I don't want to hurt Gloria."

"These childrens stronger than we think. By the way, you have one more cigarette?"

Harriet shook her head. The two sat staring ahead into the darkness.

"I have surprise that will take your mind off troubles," Lyuba said. "Ronnie dropped by. He is taking us out on town. This Friday. Will be celebration for both of us. Sophie Tucker!"

"Oh, I'm not sure," Harriet said.

"You have date?"

"Of course not."

"Then, I will not take 'no' for answer."

"All right," Harriet said. Her voice, she knew, lacked the enthusiasm that Lyuba seemed able to call upon at will.

"You are better off without Gloria's father!" She thumped a clenched hand against her breast. "He has piece of ice where heart should be."

"How do you know he has a heart of ice?"

"Will explain some day."

*

Ronnie's white convertible had the top rolled down revealing an interior color Harriet had seen only since her arrival in Miami, a fierce blue green. Lyuba ran around to the passenger side patting her hair in a showy way as if to say it would be ruined in the back seat. At the entrance to the club, customers spilled onto the sidewalk, but the maitre d', a close personal friend of Ronnie's, greeted them with a flourish. "Who do they think they are?" Harriet heard as they were led in. The small round tables, the jewels and fur stoles made Harriet wish Gloria, who appreciated all things "fancy," were here. Last week for Harriet's birthday Gloria had gone with Lyuba to Woolworth's where she had purchased a bottle of perfume, sprigs of cloth orange blossoms twined around its neck. And, it was Gloria who longed for lace, the kind that peeked from Lyuba's plunging necklines.

Ronnie ordered drinks and, before Harriet was half finished with hers, caught the waiter's attention and circling his hand over the glasses indicated they all needed another round. He leaned in close to her. "To make up for Fortune's Friend losing," he said. When Harriet gave him a puzzled look, he asked if Lyuba hadn't told her? "Damned if the odds weren't in Fortune's Friend's favor. That bum of a jockey queered the win." She had not even known the name of the horse. What a fool she had been, giving Ronnie money. "Here's to better luck!" he said. Unaware of the blush that burned her neck and cheeks, he held up his glass before taking a gulp.

By the third round, Harriet felt woozy. She watched the couples foxtrot on the wooden floor, Lyuba and Ronnie amongst them. After a long last note of the saxophone, Lyuba plopped down, fanned herself and pronounced she was famished. The waiter offered huge white menus. Tournedos of beef, Chicken Kiev, prime rib. Although Harriet had been looking forward to a steak dinner, she no longer felt like eating.

"One dance. Come on." Ronnie was standing by her chair, hand extended. She suspected Lyuba had suggested Ronnie ask her, and the thought made her feel worse, yet she could hardly refuse. The lyrics drifted out over the smoky floor. *"It seems we stood and talked like this, before. We looked at each other in the same way then, but I can't remember where or when."* Ronnie was a good dancer, and the heat of his hand made its way through the cloth of her dress. He pressed her to him, fingers moving toward the base of her spine.

"You're a very beautiful girl, you know that?" he said and, before Harriet had time to think how to answer, the bass player pulled the microphone close to his lips as if for a kiss, and announced.

"And now, the incomparable, the fabulous, the last of the red hot mamas, Sophie Tucker." Ronnie led her to her seat and, when she looked in his direction, to thank him for the dance, he was whispering in Lyuba's ear.

Her roast beef arrived, a slab of meat slung like a worn work glove over the plate. Sophie Tucker wore the dubonnet gown as promised. That dress she had hoisted onto her lap again and again as if, with each slip, it was trying to escape her clutches. She had removed her thimble and sucked on her pricked fingers to ease the smarting pain inflicted by the intricate beadwork. In the end, though, it had brought in no more money than the other dresses she had worked on.

Sophie Tucker bragged that she could come home as late as she wanted, no guy asking her where the hell she'd been. "I'm living alone and I like it," she sang over and over as she peeked out from behind her fringed shawl. A turban fixed with a large brooch sat snugly above her broad face. Lyuba laughed a raucous squawk at each strut Sophie took across the stage, her round pale calf revealed by the high side slit. Yet, Harriet wanted nothing more than to be out of her tight dress that felt so plain and shabby. No one in Miami wore beige, navy or gray, it seemed. She wanted nothing so much as to be lying in bed next to Gloria, breathing in her sweet exhalations.

When the act was over, Lyuba tucked the matches and swizzle stick in her purse so Harriet did the same. Outside, the hot humid air outside felt good after the stale odor of the air-cooled club. The car was brought around and Lyuba slipped her arm through Ronnie's taking the front seat next to him again.

It was almost one by the time they reached the hotel. The single lamp did little to soften the lobby, and a Palmetto bug squeezed itself from between the tile floor and the wall and scampered ahead.

Gloria had fallen asleep with pregnant Betty on the chaise lounge while Sasha had the bed. Gloria tangled her mother's hair in a tight fist as she carried her downstairs. "Pumpkin, Sweet pea, mommy's bunnykins," she whispered reveling in the softness of her daughter's skin.

Harriet watched the stripes from the headlights criss-cross the ceiling and slide down the walls. Gloria woke and asked for water. When Harriet rested her closed eye against her daughter's forehead, it was hot. "Mommy," Gloria said, as if reading her thoughts, "I had a dream that something bad happened."

"Nothing bad will happen. I'm here."

"Is daddy coming soon, mommy?"

Harriet stroked her daughter's forehead with a cool washcloth and promised her they would talk in the morning. When finally Gloria fell back asleep, it was a fitful one. She kicked off the sheet, awoke and called for her mother. There would be no daddy to care for them, Harriet thought, and the sooner Gloria understood this, the better. For the first time, Harriet understood the expression "heavy hearted."

In the early morning light she examined the red stamped number in the withdrawals column of her savings account book. Last week Gloria had needed new shoes, the old ones pinched so badly they had raised a blister. Her fingers searched around in her underwear and slips until they fastened upon the roll of cash she kept there. One visit to a doctor could put a real dent in her savings. She sat by the window and watched the sky grow light. When she touched her daughter's forehead again, it felt cool. She cried.

Gloria woke and touched her cheek. "Don't be sad, Mommy."

She had bought a postcard in Coral Gables and now she wrote to Doris.

Dear Doris, The friend I told you about thinks we could make crocheted pocketbooks to sell like the one you taught me to make. I think you would say getting rich is a pipe dream. How I wish we could have a cup of tea and you could give me advice! Not sure I trust myself to make judgments anymore since I am so alone. A fish out of water is appropriate for this sandy town. It must be getting cold there, but here it is always a muggy summer! Love, Harriet

*

A week after their disappointing night out, the day's sewing stowed under Lyuba's bed, the two women once again sat on the porch. Withholding cigarettes had felt unnatural to Harriet, so Lyuba helped herself. Ronnie had stopped by to tell them he had found a supplier for the materials they would need for the bags. With his connections, he could get the fancy shops to carry their pocketbooks, Lyuba said. Harriet wondered, not for the first time, how it was that Ronnie came by at times when she wasn't there. Of course, they would both have to put up some money. "He knows a place where we can get labels. Harriet and Lyuba. You like? Or Lyuba and Harriet. Which sounds best in English? I trust you in this."

"I don't know. What money I have goes to rent and food," Harriet said. "I am going to start looking for another part time job soon and Gloria will be six this summer, so she can start school."

"You must invest capital to get capital. I feel this venture golden opportunity."

"How much?"

When Harriet heard the amount, she was stunned. Surely, Lyuba didn't think she had that kind of cash. And was it possible Lyuba herself had that much money? How had she earned it? Certainly, even if she had been sewing beads for a year, she could not have saved that much. Maybe she had sewn jewels into the hem of her coat, jewels she brought from Russia. Harriet had been told stories of immigrant women who smuggled in riches to sell in the States.

Harriet thought back to the last time she had seen Ronnie. He had brought over a new batch of dresses to be decorated. She could not return his good cheer; still smarting from the much-vaunted evening on the town and her lost ten bucks.

"You could have been a fashion designer, had your own house, like Coco Chanel," he had said.

"I want house as well," Lyuba had said, her lower lip jutting out in a pout.

"A design house, baby, I mean a design house. Believe me, if I had that kind of dough, I'd stake you myself."

"We could hire other women to do crochet and beading. We think up new designs, not just pocketbooks."

Ronnie had thrown his arms around both their shoulders. "Now you've got it, kiddo." Harriet remembered how he had leaned back in his chair at the nightclub, whispering into Lyuba's ear, and the way she had turned toward him, their faces close enough to kiss.

"I have to think about this," Harriet said.

"Think, but not too hard," Lyuba answered. She stood up, arched her back and yawned dramatically, "Good night,

Darling." She must have walked a few steps into the lobby and then turned back. Harriet felt a kiss on her cheek. She startled at the gesture, the first one of real affection Lyuba had ever offered. Then she was gone.

Harriet lit one more cigarette. She had been alone before but never felt as lonely as she did now. She saw a figure coming down the street, a child, perhaps, but as he mounted the hotel steps, she recognized the man with the third leg. In the windless evening the cloth of his cape lay flat like folded wings.

"Good evening," he said. "The sky is lovely."

"Yes, it is."

He looked at her, silent, waiting.

"Would you like to sit down?" She nodded toward the seat left vacant by Lyuba.

"It is more comfortable to stand. Thank you." He tilted his head in her direction. "Your daughter loves to play with the little boy who lives here."

"I am lucky she has found a playmate."

He turned nervously as if someone were behind him. When he looked back at her, he frowned. "You should keep your eyes open with the boy's mother."

"Why do you say that?"

"Nothing in particular."

"But, you must have some reason for telling me to be careful."

"I was born with a good sense for who is worthy of trust and who is not to be trusted. Maybe I have this intuition to help me because of bad luck in other parts."

"Do you know something about Lyuba that I don't know?"

"I watch her. I watch you. You I would trust with my life."

Harriet was reminded of Lyuba's oblique claims of intuition, about her husband's cold heart and about Ronnie liking her. She had been wrong about Ronnie.

"Thank you," she said, although the compliment faded against the warning.

The next morning when she opened her door, she found a folded note on paper ripped from a notebook. "Please I am not well. Woman's trouble below. Could you take care of childrens? I will take care later."

By 5:30 Sasha announced, "I'm hungry."

"Me too," Gloria said.

She told them to wait a moment and she ran upstairs to Lyuba's. She had gone through the crackers and peanut butter and jelly and dried fruit she kept in her own room. She knocked. No answer. She knocked again and put her ear to the door. Silence.

Downstairs, she told the children that they would go to the drugstore for dinner. Each put their hands on the other's shoulders and jumped up and down yelling until Gloria fell down laughing.

After hot dogs, French fries and a glass of milk each, she returned to the hotel, knocked again on Lyuba's door, but again there was no answer. She insisted they each have baths, Sasha first. Her sadness and fear expressed itself as indulgence toward the children. She put Sasha asleep in her bed, aware that he had not once asked about his mother as if this day and night, the T-shirt Harriet offered him to sleep in, all of it had been nothing out of the ordinary. He fell asleep easily, soft snores quivering his lips.

"Is Sasha going to live with us?" Gloria asked when Harried curled herself around her.

"No. Of course not," she said. She lay awake and once Gloria's breathing evened out, she got up and went to the porch, hoping to find Lyuba in her usual chair, but their two chairs were empty.

Lyuba did not emerge from seclusion until the next morning when she knocked on the door. As soon as Sasha saw his mother, he rushed to her, the story about the sand dollar he had found, and the hot dogs they had eaten spilling out in a tumble. "Too quickly, too quickly," Lyuba said, putting her hands to her ears. "I have headache size of Texas." As usual, Sasha gave up trying to interest his mother and returned to Gloria. Lyuba thanked Harriet for "keeping an eye" on Sasha, the phrase implying that really he could very well have been fine on his own.

That night Harriet wrote a letter.

Dear Doris,

I want to tell you, as I should have before I left, what a true friend you were to me and to Gloria. No matter our love problems, we had each other and I knew you had my best interests at heart. Your wisdom and caring are missed more than I can ever say. The friend I met here, I am not so sure is really a friend. Loneliness makes one desperate and I foolishly trusted her. She wants my money, not the friendship I

longed for, a true friend you were and are. I am at sea. An-
other appropriate expression for Miami Beach.

*My life in Florida is not all sunny skies, as they want us
to believe nor is it a new lease on life. But, then maybe, nothing in life is ever how we imagined, is it?*

With love,

Harriet

She stopped and stared out the window. Strips of salm-
on streaked the sky and below it, the road was a blackened
river. She recognized the slight resemblance to the postcards displayed in the drugstore of Miami Beach at sunset.
She turned off the light.

"Mommy?" Gloria said.

"Yes, Sweetie."

"I like it here."

"That makes me very happy."

Harriet was about to say something about moving to a
bigger place, but Gloria's breathing deepened. At least she
hadn't asked about her father nor had she for a while.

Ω

Watch Me
by Rosanna Staffa

The light is off in the hallway. It's been off for a month and the first floor tenant, Mrs. Gaynor, has complained to the landlord. Over and over. She has sciatica and the beginnings of glaucoma, and believes every story she reads in the papers about muggers in the dark. She says that I don't care because I am young. Young people only read the headlines about Russia, she says. Movie reviews. Dear Abby.

Truth is, I don't have to worry about muggers because I have a beautiful left hook.

My stepfather taught it to me when I was a little girl. He took me to the park, stood with his legs wide apart and his head cocked to the side, and said:

"Hit me. Hard."

My stepfather had a thing about dinosaurs. He said they'd disappeared, babies and all. He could not get over the babies disappearing. He was going to make sure I wouldn't be taken away without putting up a fight.

Mr. Kaminsky on the second floor didn't put up a fight when he died. He was confident there was no devil in the afterlife and had no fear of dying at all. Treblinka had cured him of that. Mr. Kaminsky was absolutely sure that the devil smoked Gauloises and lived in Argentina with a couple of Dobermans. Mr. Kaminsky was very old when he finally did die. I found him at the kitchen table, his old slippers on, his right toe sticking out with a tuft of grey hair on it.

The apartment where Mr. Kaminsky lived is now occupied by a guy who vacuums his floor first thing in the morning and dry cleans all his clothes. Socks. Ties. Sheets. He doesn't like to take any chances. This new guy has complained about the light being off in the hallway. I haven't. For the last month I have been doing Scotch. I was busy.

Mr. Kaminsky and I drank Vodka. Sometimes late at night if I saw his light on I would drop by for a hand of poker. He had been in the resistance in France and still didn't sleep very much. Sometimes he woke up with a start in the middle of the night. The Nazis had dogs, his bike was thrown off the bridge, his brother was shot in the face. On those nights he let me win. Or when he remembered I was young. And a lady.

I am standing on the landing in my old robe, squinting in the dark. Ray is going on and on. On and on. He is sweating. Breathing like a dog, eyes half-closed. When I met him he looked like Al Pacino to me. Talking big. Acting bad. He got me a lease on a place. A good deal on a Honda. Cheap grass. He got me clothes at Bullock's when I got busted.

"Get off my case," I tell him, shifting my weight. "Okay? Okay. I'm not that sick yet." I just found out, I can't be that sick yet. I got dizzy this morning. Three Johns in a row. I went for a sip of water while the third one got dressed; he had a wart on his thigh. I got dizzy leaning over the sink. I saw roaches.

"Take the night off," Ray says. He is going on and on because he slept with me. Free of charge. He runs the show. He just read the test results in the hallway in the dark, after I opened the door and handed them to him. "Teresa . . ." he whines. "Teresa . . ." Like when he's coming. As if I'd done a bad thing to him personally, getting AIDS now that business was taking off.

He had gotten so freaked out he sent me to a new doctor. This one had a receptionist and people waiting on gray velvet couches.

The old doctor had worn the same shirt for the last three years, second button from the top missing. He still prescribed codeine and asked:

"How's business?"

While palpating my abdomen.

"Now Teresa, concentrate. I'll tell you the names of three horses. Pick one quick. Poseidon. Troubadour's Call. Electric Lady. It's a free Pap if you get it right."

Doing the breast exam:

"Teresa, make sure you always use a condom, okay?"

The new doctor had narrow eyes like my stepfather. He asked me:

"Any idea of who it could have been? A classmate?"

Because I wrote "student" on the *profession* dots. I could see what he had in mind: a young man with glasses dragging his skinny self to a dealer in Skid Row, then groping at me on the family couch while his folks are at the movies.

"Yeah, I have an idea," I said, and looked away at the picture of his kids in pink sweaters. "Yeah." And he felt better I could see: *We have it under control.*

I wanted to tell him, maybe it was Jake from Arkansas, whose mom calls him collect at 5:00 a.m. with a fresh psalm. Or Mr. D. He has a face like Mother Theresa; one is bound to pick up something with a face like that, something mortal to go to Heaven with.

I looked back at the doctor. I saw a little flicker in his eyes. A very small spark. Here and gone. My lips do that to men. The doctor looked at his knuckles. Then up again. He looked outside.

"Look," he said, "We are catching it a little bit late. I hope you are aware of what you could be facing." Blotched skin. Ribs sticking out. And everything. As kids, we used to chase Tony Drago down the railway tracks with stones if we caught him outside before sunset. Because of his hair, skin, lips. In our nightmare Tony would chase us through empty rooms, up winding stairs, his scarred fingers one inch from our heads.

I stood up quickly and said:

"Well, thank you doctor." I said, "Goodbye, doctor." Shook his hand as politely as if I'd sat on gray velvet couches all my life reading bouillabaisse recipes for two. I wrote him a beautiful check, with a loop at the end of the signature.

I sat on the stairs outside the doctor's office. I smoked a cigarette. I said to the street:

"Mr. Kaminsky, I'm gonna die."

*

In the dark in the hallway I sway a bit, touch Ray's hand. "Hey, Ray, come on . . ." I finger his t-shirt, eager for his smell. "Have a drink, Ray?" But he is pissed off, tight-assed about touch-sweat-saliva.

"A *drink*?" he says.

"Cheer up, Ray. Nobody's dying here." My teeth clench. "Nobody's dying. They are going to find something. Don't be an idiot." I see them looking for it, in white coats. They run up and down elevators and buses. They are very excited. I fling my robe open. "Hey, Ray. Take a good look. Come on. Cozy stuff. They line up for this. Stuff like this is made to last. Honey. *Plus*, I've got good genes. I'm made of steel. I'm so fastidious about food. Fastidious. You know that. Vegetables. Milk. That's it. No fats. No fries. Ah-ah. No. *Carrot* juice. Celery sticks."

"I used your *toilet*," Ray says, "I took a piss in your germs." His open palm sends me spinning against the rail.

"Don't be an idiot, Ray." I look up, I try to see him. His white T-shirt shining in the dark. "I'm gonna pass out," I say. I close my eyes. I'm gonna pass out. Flat. Arms out, legs out. That's what they're waiting for, the tiny germs. Waiting in the cracks of my sweat glands. Baby germs first, headlong. Like kids bursting out of school. They'll leave me

261

spread out dried out like a bear rug. My head up, teeth clenched.

"Take it easy now," I say. Easy. But Ray is gone, I pull myself up. I'm not that sick yet. Just this thing that I'm dizzy. I'm not going to pass out. When I was ten my stepfather passed out at the Greyhound terminal. Wild Turkey did that. In the dark I see him now, his purplish lips opening and closing, tongue wet.

I want Mr. Kaminsky to slide up to me, with his checkered scarf around his neck, his old robe trailing behind with a faint scent of mothballs.

"Please, Teresa. No passing out. Please. No scenes." And then I'll say:

"Okay." I'll take a very deep breath. "Thank you, Mr. Kaminsky." And I'll be calm. We'll both be calm and polite in the dark. I'll tell him: "I tried all the lipstick at the counter at May Co. They have my saliva all over 'Crimson Splendor.' I liked it special." He'll stand by me quietly. We'll breathe together. In. Out. We'll be very calm, Mr. Kaminsky and I.

I want to keep talking to Mr. Kaminsky. I want to tell him I'm doing fine now. Young executives are moving into the building but we are going to hold forth, Mr. Kaminsky. I feel brisk and efficient. Mr. Kaminsky, a walk is what's needed here. One step at a time. My hand on the rail. Ray is gone. I hold onto the rail. Ray is gone. I'm Teresa five years old. In the dark on the top step holding on to the rail. Mom is at her night shift at Burger King. My stepfather is drunk in the hallway.

"Teresa . . ." he whispers in the dark. "Teresa, is that you?" I stand very still, without breathing. "Is that you up there?" he is moving along the wall, slowly. "Teresa."

I say:

"Please." I say, "Don't touch me."

"Yeah," he says, "come on down, honey baby."

I dreamed of spiders for years. They came in the dark. One by one. With big eyes staring in the dark. Long hairy legs. Touching me.

*

My stepfather had a thing about dinosaurs. He said they disappeared. Babies and all. He couldn't get over the babies disappearing. He didn't want to give up on the babies. He woke me and my brother up in the middle of the night, to look under our blankets for them. He sat in the kitchen in the dark, with a bottle of Scotch and a flashlight, waiting for a rustle.

Last time I saw him, he came to bail me out. It was a long time ago, before Ray was around. He bought me coffee, paying with change. Mom's money. He looked short. I said to him:

"I think about you."

"Thank you," he said.

In the dark I breathe deeply. In. Out. I might not go for a walk after all. I might slide down right here. Let go of myself. Slide. Fold down. Flat. Yes. I slide onto Mrs. Gaynor's welcome mat. Right under Mrs. Gaynor's door, by the den where she keeps a carpet from her sister Daureen who became a Maryknoll nun and needs no furniture. And I'm going to lie here flat. Let them get me. Among Mrs. Gaynor's cats. Warm. Quiet. Get me now. With Mrs. Gaynor chatting, sipping vervain infusion: "I wish I had my eyes back. I'd watch TV. I'd laugh when they say: "This is *my* mother!"

"You go ahead and leave, Ray!" I holler. "You go ahead and do it. You're gonna come back begging!"

Watch me. And I pull myself up. My head up. Watch me, Ray. He likes me special when I walk. High heels and tight ass.

The entrance door is open. The new guy in the building is standing there. His dry-cleaned shirts rustling in cellophane.

"Have you got a cigarette?" I say. He keeps staring at me. My robe is open. He sees my breasts. He sees the tiny mole by my belly button. He pulls a cigarette out of his pocket. He takes his sweet time doing it.

"Any matches?" I ask. He doesn't answer. I shrug. "Hey, you got no matches, it's alright. Hey, thanks."

I walk on steady. I give him a full view of me swaying the way I do, that drives Ray crazy, begging. It's my thank-you note, dry-clean baby.

If I pass that light before I count five I'm gonna die old with Ray. Me and him. We open a house. A class act. We are old and he takes pills for his back pain.

Ω

Counting
by Jodi Barnes

She learned like everyone else: the ordinal naming of fingers and toes, red M&Ms, Lego and puzzle pieces. Dreaded peas on her plate, days until Santa, pennies in her plastic pig, peonies on grandmother's bushes. Holding her breath, the consonants in *rhythm*, the miles between her parents' houses. All the books she'd ever read, crushes, then after the accident, her real friends.

For six years she's counted on their pity. Today she wheels across soft patches of green and brown to her grandmother's headstone. Perched there, a lark. In its beak a tiny heart-shaped petal, the same pinkish purple on her toenails prom night. It took seven months for the last paint chip to disappear. She looks down at her Spiderman sneakers: Decorations, like her legs.

Often she dreams she doesn't get into her dead boyfriend's car. She dances solo in her stupor and calls her mother who'd promised, "I'll pick you up; no questions asked." In the dream she opens the passenger door, throws up on the driveway. Late morning she stumbles out into sunshine, head throbbing, to hose down the drive.

Now when she wakes, she holds her breath, not knowing which dream she's in. She counts to ten before failing to swing her legs to the floor. She's sick of dreams, useless legs and calculations. Infinite what-ifs bear down like a heavy wheel.

Something stirs in the trees. As the lark begins to lift, she's moved by its idle feet, that it's all in the wings.

Ω

Circumstances
by Camille Griep

By the time they pull you out of the car, the party is already half over. Harry from accounting has mown through the good cheese and the VP is opening the evening's lesser quality wines. Your cubicle neighbor has checked her watch twice, noting the unlikelihood of your tardiness. Your nemesis jokes you had to pick the right bow tie to make your entrance. Luella stares into her empty glass thinking she misunderstood.

She's the one they call later, a cheerful ring tone ripping through deep layers of red wine sleep. Hers is the only number on the recent calls list, save the Chinese place on 3rd. She hangs up, heart slamming, limbs electric with pins and needles. The two of you are still only a possibility. She doesn't know whether to cry.

You refuse visitors. You wouldn't be able to tell them anyway. You were thinking about brie and champagne, a glinting ding on the beige car too close, driver slumped over the wheel. Metal shrieked and twisted, steam hissing white streams through billows of black tire smoke, a unique sound you can't un-hear. You obsess over that final minute, dreaming alternate endings.

Luella attributes your solitude to stoicism instead of the necklace of surgical chain culminating in a garish, glistening trache and humiliating yellow tube snaking from the bed. You don't call anyone.

Still, she buys roses. She pauses at your closed door. For another few seconds, she remains innocent of circumstances beyond anybody's control.

Ω

Visitation Rights
by Dino Parenti

On the weekends I was allowed to be with him, Pop and I would shoot guns.

He'd pick me up from Mama's early Saturday while she slept, always waiting in his truck down the street and staring down the sun while gnashing on a spicebush twig. We'd have hot biscuits, then drive an hour to all the repo-houses near the levies were we'd bleed the day unloading buckshot and thirty-ought slugs into boarded-up domiciles. The reports exploded the abandoned silence, flushing out eddies of grackles and terns, and as my ears screamed, the wail of shattering wood and glass never failed to drive air into Pop's shoulders while seeping it from the veins that had come to grip his neck.

Pop never talked while we shot. In fact we hardly spoke but a few words on Saturdays; that's what Sundays were for. I guess he still smarted over losing the house, but at night when he would whistle at the moon and pull from a battered flask, I'd see the glint in his eyes splinter into a dozen glints, all flashing the warmer hues of the spectrum.

We'd end our Saturdays by shooting up the old Victorian by the place where the ladies danced wearing only what looked to me then as party favors. Afterwards, our loads spent, Pop would stare at the juke-joint for a long while before calling it a night. Sometimes he'd mutter Mama's name. Sometimes, he'd just whistle at the neon rippling in the puddles.

Ω

Give Me Your Wife

by Tony Hoagland

GIVE me your
wife because
I like her. I like

the signs of wear on her;
the way her breasts have dropped a little with the years;
the weathered evidence of joy around her eyes.

I like her faded jeans,
her hennaed hair;
her hips pried open by the child.

I find her interesting; her grey-eyed
calm of a resigned sea;
her stillness like a painting on the wall.

It's not that you don't care,
but after all, you're just a man
who has been standing in

water up to his neck for years,
and never managed to quite
dunk his head entirely under.

So give me your wife. Recycle her.
Look at her mouth, like a soft dry rose;
the way she stands, at an angle

to the world.
She could still be kissed and joked with,
teased into a bed

with cool white sheets;
convinced to lie and be
laid down upon.

Happiness might
still find a place
for her.

Give me your wife
like you were
unbuttoning something
accidentally

and leaving it behind.
Then just drift away
and let me try.

Ω

Bessie Arrowood's Circle of Life
by Karen Paul Holmes

Circumambulation: The act of walking around something in a circle,
especially for a ritual purpose

THERE she goes again, spinning
her wheelchair 'round the nursing home.
Two years, five thousand laps. So far.
With God's help, she says, *I'll reach*
eight thousand by this time next year.

Politely, the small town *Sentinel*
doesn't give Bessie's age nor why
she entered the home six years ago.
In her picture, a cannula helps her breathe,
yet she supplies her own determined air.

Neither wind, nor rain, nor oxygen tank
stops Bessie from what she calls her *project*—
I call it her prayer, her lifesaver.
More boomerang than arrow,
Bessie completes herself with each round.

Ω

This Isn't Silverlake Anymore
by Neil McCarthy

"Send lawyers guns and money, the shit has hit the fan."
—Warren Zevon

1.

IN a different life I'd run away with the waitress,
scream across Santa Monica Boulevard negligent of red
     lights.
In a different time I'd perhaps get her to take the wheel
while I shoot out the tires of the pursuing cop cars,
confident of making the border before nightfall.

We'd lie low in Tijuana, maybe cut and dye each other's
     hair
and mull over the maps and the madness of our options.
Bolivia might come into the equation. As might Honduras,
which would be less of a drive and warmer at night.
It might then be time to dump the stolen Cadillac.

Back in LA, the news headlines would make my colleagues
giddy with perversion.

In a smoky room a phone would ring,
the receiver lift and a voice on the other end announce
in excitement *Mac's made it.*

2.

Desires crackle like moths to a hot bulb in this café,
the scripts abandoned and
the headshots growing older by the day.
They still dress the part mind you, the waitress in her
    bowler hat and black bra visible through her thin
white cotton blouse;
my neighbor in his striped three-piece suit and pocket
    watch.

I was told about the ice-cream parlor across the street and
I shift my attention, watching the clientele come and go,
when all of a sudden it's you that's on the run.
You are dressed to the nines, dark sunglasses and bouncy
    hair,
men wait until you have passed before turning to inhale
the slipstream of your perfume—

      —it's Florence. It's early summer. There you are.

In front of a cathedral, pigeons scatter as *Carabinieri* race
towards the bank alarm calling out for help, but you? You
just light a cigarette and toss the match stick over your

shoulder. It's all being shot in black and white of course to
give that timeless sense,
while from an open balcony window we can hear a cello
play the Bach preludes as the credits roll
    and you disappear into the foreground.

3.

I hear the slightly scratched voice of Joan Baez coming from
the record player
singing about the junipers in the pale moonlight,
applause erupting like hailstones on a corrugated iron roof.
I am singing back through the bedroom wall,
wishing the neighbours would just shut up for once
    and listen.

Night arrives with a baton, taking its dark lectern on cue
    and conducting its flotilla of noise:
fire trucks, police sirens, ambulances,
a car alarm crying wolf to the night.

Headlights, red lights, green lights, turning signals, cross-
    walks flashing,
gas station forecourt lights; Sunset Boulevard from this
    angle looks more
like a fallen Christmas tree.

And I am reading your email, throwing my mind back to
    the wine bar

tables where we would arm wrestle over the colors:
misty-memory-green, winter-cheek-red—
each new phrase coined
    celebrated like a scientific breakthrough.

In a different life I would run away with you,
into the tattoo-blue of early evening, cover our tracks
and burn every single one of those maps.

$$\Omega$$

The Reincarnation of the Seagull
by Lisa Pellegrini

BEFORE he was a seagull
he was the bed of the ocean,
its stronghold and place of

penance, a tenderfoot of sorts.
Before he was the ocean bed
he was the salt that glittered
on the crests of rhythmic waves,

infusing sea kelp and sea urchins
with sustenance and secrecy.
Before he was the salt he was
the tail of a clown fish that

two piranhas wrestled over
in a claustrophobic frenzy.
He was fragments of barnacles,
scallop shells, and coral reefs

that fell out of a cave's mouth
faster than candy spilling forth
from a piñata. He was the patches
of aqua that comprised the sky's

mosaic quilt before the sun
was crowned king, after the
moon clothed herself in a
shroud of seclusion and sobriety.

$$\Omega$$

Prone to Manic Episodes After a Motorcycle Crash

by Luke Patterson

HE was twenty years old with dark eyes.
I will write *patient suffers from*
paranoid delusion in my run report
and later just call him *crazy*

to my partner as we smoke cigarettes
outside, drinking diet coke from the EMT
room and thinking about how the post-
surgical degeneration of his left arm

has made it look disparate, a foreign limb
hanging opposite the muscular uninjured right.
I note also the *lateral anterior suture on the frontal*
cranium that rises in a pale crease of *(scar)* tissue

just above mistrustful dark eyes. I will later
resolve to never buy a motorcycle,

as we drive bright and loud
toward other eyes, other scars,

the city surrounding us, pressing
up tight against ambulance doors.

Ω

Günther's Tree
by Lois P. Jones

BECAUSE you are strong.
Because your branches span out ahead of you.

And in so many years, age has allowed breadth to match
    height.
Boughs so heavy with time they touch the ground.

Because a crow can land as easily as the butterfly
and a bench so perfectly placed beneath you

is shelter from the heat. Because all I want is to sleep
under your canopy. To dream of families that feasted

on acorns, cooked quail and rabbit on soft ground
near your roots. Because you sit amongst the hundreds

of fragrant roses and the white arbor overlooking
an English garden—amid the bee palm and hibiscus

with its orderly wildness. I cannot distinguish water
that rushes over the fountain's stones from the wind in your
   leaves.

And this is music.
And there is a shelter like Mahler's little hut
where the occasional deer can wander, curious.

$$\Omega$$

The Spoken World
by Brett Garcia Rose

Here are the rules: You must begin every sentence or phrase with a vowel. Any word beginning with a consonant is considered high risk and must be preceded without pause by a vowel ending in a higher tonality. This is the roller-coaster. The letters *M*, *B*, *G* and *V* are especially troublesome. Avoid them, substitute with words beginning in a *Z* or *TH* or another soft consonant where possible (hint: you can get away simple letter substitution within a word if you fake a yawn or hiccup), but if you need to use them you will always and carefully place them towards the end of the sentence, when you are out of breath and have the necessary speed and force to break through. This is the run. You can never use words that begin with *T*, *S*, *Y* or a hard *C*, and you can never use any word containing an audible *W* or a soft *U*. These sounds are unavailable to you. Find alternatives.

Now construct a paragraph describing what you did today. You have 2 minutes.

A stutterer learns to do this at five years old. By the time we reach nine we can do it in around half a second. At 12 we have the mental equivalent of a college-level thesaurus and will often use three or four syllable words or entire phrases in place of a single word containing a letter we cannot use. A common example is for us to say "I'd prefer not to agree at the moment," instead of a simple "no," if the word stutters in the internal rehearsal that takes place in the moments prior to verbalizing.

We speak the way writers write, and we edit in real time. And even though the lag lessens with time and practice, a stutterer will likely go his or her entire life without ever having a real conversation. We are three steps ahead of ourselves at all times. We cannot enjoy the present because you can't bear the silence. We love and fear and respect language in ways the fluents could never imagine. We think in words, not images, because we are necessarily obsessed with the delivery of our thoughts more so than their contents, and we are so preoccupied with our verbal puzzles that there is no room for anything else. And although we may only speak 30 or 40 words in a given week, we have a constant stream of dialogue running through our minds. Life, for us, is an ongoing rehearsal.

School is a problem beginning at a very early age, but not because of the social abuses put upon us. Those are not unique to stutterers, and we learn to take it just as any other outcast groups of children do. Fat, ugly, pimply, speechless, it doesn't make a difference. Children are mean, and there is never a shortage of targets. No, we are inevitably undone by our own cleverness, our self-cures. We develop many simple and complicated ways to avoid speaking. The survival of a young stutterer depends on his or her ability to avoid attention, to eliminate the reasons and opportunities to speak. As long as we're allowed to keep silent, we believe we're just like everyone else. Much of this involves simply becoming smaller; if we cannot get something on our own then we just learn to not want it. We spend our entire lives going around things others take for granted, things they look forward to.

We don't make friends. We don't date. We don't fall in love. We take whatever jobs we can find, because we don't interview.

But we do speak, and we are proud when we speak well. One sentence well delivered means as much to us as an entire graduation speech means to the valedictorian. Our speech is funny, sure, stilted and put together wrong even when properly rehearsed and delivered, but it's the only speech we have. And no, we are not grateful when you complete our thoughts for us. We want to murder you. My father, of all people, understood this. People were routinely thrown out of our house for less.

Stuttering is not a handicap. There are no stickers or scholarships for us. We get the opposite of special treatment. Teachers often take it upon themselves to cure us of this annoying and disruptive problem, either by brute force or shame. And so, predictably, we fail, and then we rebel to justify our failures, and eventually succumb to the escalating, negative descriptors put upon us. I could not speak, so I learned to pick pockets and locks. Such was my story, and it is a common one among stutterers. We fail, yet we are not failures.

After nearly dropping out of high school, my father gave me the typical ultimatum of the day, either go to college or get out. It was understood that I was basically retarded and would go no farther. My family was tired. I was tired. We'd all had enough. I'd find a good life as a mechanic or line cook somewhere. I'd live the same blue-collar life the rest of my family did before me. I'd learn a trade. There was no shame in this.

Only, I didn't. Perhaps it was my lifelong anger at stuttering, at my father, at the world. Perhaps it was just fear of leaving. I still don't know. But I never felt stupid, regardless of all evidence and assurances to the contrary. I wasn't book smart in any sense, but I could think. So I applied to the only school that would take me, a local two year community college with no admission requirements and cheap tuition. I enrolled for one semester, five classes, and received a perfect score in every one. Another interesting fact about stutterers; we don't really need to study. We spend our entire lives listening to others speak, and we do it well.

Much to their credit and my own minor astonishment, my family was not surprised at all, and faithfully supported me throughout my difficult college career. Without their unyielding, unforgiving strength I'd have gone no further than high school. There were still many important classes where I received unsatisfactory grades, or simply removed myself and failed when presented with forced participation. And worse, instructors easily notice students who under-perform and either go hard or give up. To the sensibilities of the outside world, we are either retarded or rebellious, and sandbagged accordingly. University is not so different from grade school in this respect. But I trudged on. For my father, mostly. Sometimes I excelled, often I failed, but I never received an average grade. And I never quit.

I stumbled onto writing by accident. Classes with heavy emphasis on written assignments were easy for me, so long as I did not have to read aloud (I often got the flu and lost my "voice"), yet I did not think about writing until I began to keep a journal; well, really, until someone important to me discovered my journal and read it in secret. She confronted me a hundred pages in, laughing and crying and questioning. She'd never known I had so much to say. Anything, really, to say. She was, and remains, the most beautiful person I have ever met.

We were engaged to be married a few months later. Several months after that I was the youngest person ever to publish a column in *The Sunday Newsday Magazine*. Three times.

Thus began my brief career in journalism. At my second school, after a year of no friends, no parties, nothing, I wrote a goodbye story and slipped it under the door of the campus newspaper's office late one night, a sad farewell to people I'd never known but desperately wanted to, people I'd watched with envy and admiration and genuine warmth. I wrote a goodbye letter to the student I'd never be, to the people who I would never know. By the time it was published I was long gone. At my next school, a larger, state school, I'd publish a weekly column for two years under a pen name. I discovered, then, that I was not just writing for one person; I could write for everyone. That person was famous. People wanted to know me. They'd invite me to parties, ask for my thoughts, for my friendship, for my love. Everyone wanted to know that person. But I'd never have anything to say. The person they wanted to talk to didn't exist yet. It was time, again, for me to go.

And so I'd transfer again, just leave in the middle of the night, no one to say goodbye to, no one to wish me well or to hold me back. I'd transfer again. And again. At each school I'd publish fiction for the college literary magazines, essays for the journals, columns for the newspapers. At Northeastern University, where I finally graduated, I kept a part-time job cleaning the newsroom, ever aware of my mounting debts. After each production cycle, I'd work overnight scraping the wax from the floors and layout boards for seven dollars an hour. When someone finally connected me as the wax guy to me as the columnist in the same paper, to the fiction writer in the literary magazine, to the essayist, I was offered leadership editorial positions of increasing responsibility, and one of the few regrets I carry with me was that I never accepted any of them. I was becoming a good writer and an excellent researcher, sure, but the inability to use a telephone made the task all but impossible. No one texted back then. No one emailed. I was tired of failing.

I was good with computers, however, and my last few months in school I was instrumental in budgeting and implementing a conversion to full electronic publishing. My advisors thought I was autistic, but they accepted my plan wholesale, and I made it work. Three months later the university newspaper, one of the largest student papers in the country at the time, was fully electronic. No more wax. My job was done. My final effort as a journalism student was to shed my weekly column and write a three part, front page investigative series on animal research and abuse on campus, resulting in a suspension of federal funding for the university biology department, and significant disciplinary action against me. I'd been funny in the past, literary, romantic even. Now I had teeth. But it was worth every word. I went on to become an underground writer and researcher for the animal rights movement, and eventually became production editor of the Animal's Agenda, the international magazine of animal rights activism. My journalism, however, would go no further. Eventually, someone would always ask me a question. And laugh at my non-answer.

At the same time I also entered general electronic publishing, designing layouts for Popular Mechanics, Redbook, Windows Magazine, MacMillan trade books and other publications, but this, too, was a short-lived career. I was summarily ejected due to another small handicap I had kept hidden; I am colorblind, and inevitably made a costly mistake on a central layout. Colleagues covered for me initially, but people only go so far. Thus ended my career in writing and publishing.

So I went to a trade school on a federal assistance program and learned software engineering. I studied database theory at Columbia University in the evenings. In 1995 I started my own company, inventing a system called Concept-Tel for the wholesale telecommunications industry. I am the sole employee, designer, developer, salesperson and CEO, and continue in this capacity today. My closest competitor has nearly forty employees, and yet I succeed well enough, and often excel. Other times I fail, go broke, work for other companies. But I'm used to that. A stutterer learns failure at about the same time other children Lego.

Still, all these years later, I wish I had found a way to stay the course. I wish I had kept writing every single day, as I did then. I wish I had the courage to not bend to the world. I wish I could still talk to that young woman who discovered me, who gave me my first chance to communicate with the world. It was not my stutter that ended my writing career. It was not the misinformed teachers and counselors and therapists. It was not the meanness of my peers. It was not my parents. It was me. The world had not beaten me. It had challenged me. What everyone saw as my success was, to me, a profound failure. I'd spent a lifetime avoiding the very thing that had saved me. My writing.

Like so many others, I began writing out of despair and a sense of disconnectedness from the world, out of loneliness and fantasy. In my writing I was fluid and fluent, I could be charming or terrifying or wise. In my writing I had friends and purpose and value. I was someone to talk to, someone to love. In my writing, I discovered myself. In discovering myself, I came to know the world.

Eventually I overcame my stutter and evolved into the speaking superhero that I had so often fantasized about, but I still write for the same basic reason. Like someone who moves into a new home and renovates it to their liking, I recreate the world I inhabit through my fiction, and although my changes are often small and subtle, when I am finished and read back what I have written, that world seems like a better place than before. My characters are lonely, though. They don't talk much. They don't need to. But in all my work, and my life in general, there is that unyielding, ever-present loneliness that all stutterers share, and the profound power that accompanies its presence. I do think this is a common path that many writers take; it begins as a curiosity, then an art, then an outlet, then an addiction and finally an immersive way of life. To a stutterer, it is a lifeline, no less important to us than air or water or love. For me, though, the real world is indistinguishable from fiction, and the more I write, the greater control I gain over that fictional world, which directly translates into greater power over my own life.

I learned to shed the thick skin I'd developed as a stutterer. I overcame all of that tremendous anger that all stutterers bear. In the end, it served no purpose. I deserve and demand from the universe no less than anyone else. After many years I'd come to learn what others accept as children. All you have to do, is ask. The world is only as frightening as you allow it to be.

So two years ago I'd finally done what I'd always feared, what I'd always found a way around and made silent excuses for. An editor of a magazine that published some of my work asked me to read in public. I said no, but he just told me the date, and how long I was to read for. I was a writer, he'd said at the time. This is what writers do. He knew nothing of my stutter, and still doesn't, but assumed that this was a fear all new writers had to deal with. I was to compete in Literary Death Match, next to successful writers, in front of famous judges. I had weeks to prepare, and seven minutes to read.

I invited my family. I'd memorized every word of my story so I would not have to deal with paper. My plan, all along, was to announce up front that I was a stutterer, that I was nervous, that I would do my best. I would ask for patience, for lenience and acceptance. Once on stage, however, I did no such thing. I looked at the lights and the judges, at the hundreds of waiting faces in the audience, at my family. I just started reading, and I read slowly, confidently. I read well. When it was over, I'd expected my family to be astonished, to be proud and amazed at the words coming from my mouth, for no such thing had ever seemed even remotely possible to me. My mother commented that I sounded like I had a southern accent. People talked with me late into the night and, for the first time, I answered. The next morning, the Miami Herald published excerpts from my story. There was no mention of any horrible speech problems or people laughing or booing. None of it happened. And I realized, at that moment, that I was no longer a stutterer. My family had forgotten. My audience never knew. Even the journalists couldn't figure it out. I was, simply, a writer. The stutterer was gone.

I read my work in public now from time to time, and am heckled and critiqued as all writers are, but never for my speaking. Every word I utter is a profound victory. I am a writer and a speaker, no better or worse than any other. No one need know I was ever a stutterer. And I have no more pity for those who stutter than for those who can't write. Personally, if I had to choose, and I remember when I was forced to, I'd choose writing. Every time.

I have the same insecurities as any other person now. I feel unprepared, at times unworthy and exceptionally lucky, and yet I know there is more to it. For no matter the success I find in software, it is insignificant to the pride I take in writing, and the pure exhilaration I feel when I am able to write well, to finish a good story or even a page in one, and to know that it is mine, mine alone and hard-won. I give no further thought to speaking. Whatever I have to say, I say.

And so I return to my beginning as a writer. To write regularly, to understand the craft and trade more completely. To become, finally, a writer, as corny as that may sound. It is difficult and at times frustrating and disheartening; I am a young writer and largely self-taught, with all of the bad habits and insecurities that come with that meandering and unstructured effort. Yet I continue, I persevere, in the same way I have in my career in activism, in my software, in my stuttering, and in my life.

I'll never be that person who comes through my writing. None of us ever are. We pass one another at times, these two eager selves, we nod and acknowledge each other as peers, as equals, distinct and ever distant yet, in the end, friends. The spoken world is bigger than I had ever imagined it to be, wonderful and relentless and unforgiving, and to be a part of it was my grandest childhood fantasy. I don't know what the world sees me as now, just another guy trudging along the same road, at once careful and reckless as we all are. I still don't speak much, and I find the world every bit as mean as I did when I was a child. Inside I will always be a stutterer, with all of the wonderful gifts and peculiarities and sadness earned as such. But outside? In the big real world I had hidden from so well and for so long? Outside, I'm just another writer, struggling to find words, to be heard and understood and absorbed. Searching, at long last, for something to say.

*

"The Spoken World" originally appeared in *Rose and Thorn Journal*.

Ω

Choose Me

by Erica Orloff

I read an interview with a Buddhist holy man in which he said a miscarriage is a sign that the soul of that baby-to-be had a change of heart, perhaps was not ready to be reborn. Or perhaps chose a different mother.

Of course, for me, always dancing on the precipice of self-doubt as a mom, I took the loss of the baby as a sign I was not chosen. And so November came—the month the baby was to be born, and I took to my bed with an angst-filled heart.

It didn't help, of course, that my oldest child, in the throes of adolescence, declared me "the most eccentric mother in the universe!" *This* was why the baby didn't choose me, I reasoned. I hate to cook. I hate to clean. The stacks of clutter rise from my desk—and the floor around my desk. And the shelves *adjacent* to my desk. I read a book on anti-cluttering that said to attack your "hot spots" of clutter. I look around, and if hot spots are any indication, my house is on fire.

The laundry spills from the laundry room into the hallway. And then there are the pets. At any given time—depending on species longevity—we have mice, frogs, beta fish, goldfish, cats, and birds. And a hedgehog. And my son's python. And a rabbit. Named Lola. Who we thought was a girl but turned out to be a boy.

And dogs. Misbehaving dogs that don't sit on command. And like to eat toilet paper.

And me. At my desk writing when I should be the PTA mom. But PTA moms scare me a little. My house is too loud in addition to being too messy. My friends are incorrigible sorts, not soccer moms. They are writers and artists and other eccentrics, and the kids' gay uncle who comes over in bunny slippers—I sense a rabbit theme here. Bella's godmother has purple hair. And there is the cacophony of music—the tuba, piano, violin, cello. And dust bunnies. Along with Lola.

My oldest was right. Eccentric with a capital E. The nights and weeks of insomnia, me writing furiously at 2:00 a.m. then using pots of coffee in daylight hours to barely function as a mother. The distractedness when I am mid-novel. The lack of simply activities of daily living—like showers—when I am on deadline. Who would choose me?

And so I grieved. The miscarriage was early in the pregnancy, but I had already named the baby in my heart. Talked to it. Was so *certain* this soul chose me. Only it changed its mind.

And I couldn't blame the baby. Who would choose me?

Months later, though past forty, I decide maybe I will try again. Maybe there was a soul waiting in the Universe who didn't mind dust bunnies and a messy mother who cannot make macaroni and cheese even out of the blue box. And even if my teen daughter at that moment kind of loathed me, the two other kids sort of liked me, right? Surely, a soul wanted rebirth in my handy little womb.

And on the first try, the little pregnancy stick indicated ding-ding-ding—ladies and gentlemen, we have a baby.

So who chose me?

By age six, the child who chose me was discussing how to hotwire and steal his first car. It's been years of nonstop mayhem since he entered the world. This child, I suppose now with a Buddhist perspective, chose the mother who would be right for him. Even the pediatrician, when I told her how he hurled a gallon of maple syrup off the second-story landing to see if the plastic container would break open (it did) at age two (!), said, "This child is lucky he has a mother who's a novelist. Who *gets* him."

When he went through his age-three refusal-to-bathe stage, the only way water could touch his skin was by telling him it was a ninja ritual to cleanse himself before battle. I constantly try to outwit his eccentricities. The food that cannot touch the other food. His sensory issues—for a year the only pants he would wear were fuzzy fleece—and if not them, then constant nudity. The day he walked across the street, dropped trou and peed on the nice grandmother's rose bush. While she stood there watching.

The rotting jars of "experiments"—strange concoctions of food and liquid and for all I know bodily fluids. The time he fed the dog with irritable bowel syndrome Raisin Bran. His worm collection. Including the ones he put on my pillow at bedtime. And in my glass of wine. Congealed worm slime in Chardonnay. The time he wanted to dig up the deceased and buried hedgehog to see if we could reanimate it into a zombie hedgehog. He frightens me. I have to bury pets in the middle of the night so he can't locate them.

He curses like a sailor (past life?) and mastered the armpit fart by age three. He has taken apart both my vacuum cleaner and the intake system for the air conditioning unit in the time it took me to shower. He likes tools. Power tools. And the collection of leftover nuts and bolts I find in his pockets have me questioning at what point will I sit on something to have it collapse beneath me. He is *never* getting a chemistry set.

When I ask him what he wants to be when he grows up, he tells me a criminal mastermind or evil ruler of the free world. Complete with minions.

Sometimes, he is so wild and destructive, I simply collapse in a chair and cry.

And then he comes over to me, pushes my now-unruly hair from my face (I pull at my hair so often in frustration, I wonder why I am not bald by this point), and says, "I try to be good, Mommy, but it's just not in me."

"I must be the world's worst mother if I cannot get one little kindergartener to behave and not drop the f-bomb."

"No. You are the perfect mother. The best one. *For me.*"

And there it is.

Each November, I light a candle to the baby that changed its mind. I wish its little soul well. I wonder if that baby was reborn into a fine, upstanding family. One with a mother who can cook. A home free of dust bunnies and clutter hot spots. A family that is quiet. With one pet. A dog that sits on command. And my heart aches for just a moment.

And then usually something crashes. And I am screaming the name of the boy who did choose me. I know I have circles under my eyes since his arrival. And my house is messier than ever, with unusual stains in the carpets and crayon murals on the walls.

And I know he found the right womb. The right mother.

He chose me.

Ω

Contributors

JODI BARNES'S flash fiction can be found at *100 Word Story*, *Tupelo Quarterly*, *Prime Number*, *Wigleaf's* Top 50, *Camroc Press Review*, and Fictionaut Editor's Eye. Her short-short stories have made finalist at *Glimmer Train*, *Sixfold*, and in *Press 53's* Open Awards. Her chapbook, *unsettled* (Main Street Rag), was runner-up for the 2010 Oscar Arnold Young Award for best poetry book in North Carolina. She founded 14 Words for Love, small literary acts for social good. Jodi is a writer-in-residence for North Carolina schools and she teaches writing, social justice, social identity and their connections.

DAVID BUCHANAN is PhD candidate at the University of Denver and he used to fly tanker aircraft in the Air Force. He writes about growing up in a small town and growing old in the military. His short fiction has appeared in *War, Literature, & the Arts*, *The Writer's Workshop Review*, *Line of Advance*, and *O-Dark Thirty: The Report*.

JUSTIN CAMPBELL won the 2013 Zora Neale Hurston / Richard Wright Foundation Award for African American Writers. His work has appeared or is forthcoming in *The Millions, The African American Review, The Cossack Review, 34th Parallel Literary Magazine*, and elsewhere. He is a regular contributor to "The Two Cities," a theology and culture blog.

MALCOLM R. CAMPBELL is the author of *Sarabande, The Sun Singer, Jock Stewart and the Missing Sea of Fire, The Seeker, The Sailor*, and *The Betrayed*.

SUZANNE CONBOY-HILL earned a PhD from University College London and pursued a career in psychology before turning to fiction; earning in 2014 an MA in Creative Writing from Lancaster University. Her stories have appeared in *Every Day Fiction, Boomunderground, Zouch Magazine, Full of Crow, Ether Books*, and elsewhere.

MATTHEW COREY is a fiction writer and essayist living in Brooklyn. His work has appeared or is forthcoming in *Turtle Point Press Magazine* and *Pequod*.

CAMILLE GRIEP lives and writes in the Pacific Northwest. Her fiction has been featured in dozens of online and print journals, as well as anthologized in collections including *Witches, Stitches, & Bitches* (Evil Girlfriend Media), *The Sea* (Dark Continents Press), and *Unidentified Funny Objects* (UFO Publishing). She is a senior editor at *The Lascaux Review* and serves on the board of Cascade Writers. Her first novel will be released in Summer 2015 from 47North.

TONY HOAGLAND'S poems and essays have appeared widely. He is the author of several collections including *Donkey Gospel*, winner of the James Laughlin Award, and *What Narcissism Means to Me*, finalist for the National Book Critics Circle Award. He teaches creative writing at the University of Houston and at Warren Wilson College.

KAREN PAUL HOLMES is the author of the poetry collection *Untying the Knot* (Aldrich Press, 2014). She received an Elizabeth George Foundation emerging writer grant in 2012. Publishing credits include *Poetry East, Atlanta Review, Caesura, POEM, The Sow's Ear Poetry Review, Every Day Poems, The Southern Poetry Anthology Vol 5: Georgia*, and the forthcoming anthology of Georgia poets from Negative Capability Press.

LOIS P. JONES'S work has appeared in *The American Poetry Journal* and numerous other markets, domestic and abroad. She is the host of Poets Cafe on KPFK in Los Angeles (Pacifica Radio), poetry editor of *Kyoto Journal*, and a four-time Pushcart nominee and Best New Poets nominee.

JOE KAPITAN'S first story collection, *A Pocket Guide to North American Ghosts*, was published in 2013. His work has appeared in *Wigleaf, Matter Press, Midwestern Gothic, A cappella Zoo, The Cincinnati Review, McSweeney's*, and other journals.

NEIL MCCARTHY is an Irish poet who divides his time between California and Europe. His poems have appeared in over 30 international journals and anthologies, including *The New York Quarterly*, *The Cortland Review*, *Magma* (UK), and *Poetry Salzburg Review* (Austria). In 2013 he released his first spoken word CD, *Live in the Laden*, recorded in Vienna. He can be found at neilmccarthypoetry.com.

LINDA MCCULLOUGH MOORE is the author of the novel *The Distance Between* and the short story collection *This Road Will Take Us Closer to the Moon*, about which Alice Munro wrote, "These stories won me over at once, heart and mind together." Her short work has appeared in *The Massachusetts Review*, *Glimmer Train*, *The Boston Globe*, *The Alaska Quarterly Review*, *House Beautiful*, *The Sun*, *The Southern Review*, and numerous other venues. She has been a winner or finalist in many national awards including New York Stories, The Nelson Algren Award, The Tobias Woolf Award, and The Pushcart Prize XXXV.

DONNA MISCOLTA is the author of *When the de la Cruz Family Danced*, published by Signal 8 Press in 2011. Her work has appeared in *Hawaii Pacific Review*, *Connecticut Review*, *Waxwing*, and elsewhere. Awards include the Bread Load/Rona Jaffe Scholarship for Fiction, and grants from 4Culture, Artist Trust, and Seattle City Artists. She was a runner-up for the Grace Paley Prize in Short Fiction and a finalist for the Flannery O'Connor Award for Short Fiction.

MARIA MUNRO-SCHUSTER is a middle school teacher in Bozeman, Montana. "Settling Gwendolyn" is her first short story publication.

ERICA ORLOFF is the author of over 20 novels for adults, young adults, and (as Erica Kirov) middle-grade readers. A native New Yorker, she currently resides in Virginia.

DINO PARENTI is an architectural draftsman whose short works have appeared in *Pantheon Magazine*; *Cease, Cows*; *The Lascaux Review*; and elsewhere.

LUKE PATTERSON lives and works in Houston, Texas.

LISA PELLEGRINI resides in Warrington, Pennsylvania. Her poetry has been published in *Zouch Magazine, Downer Magazine, The Rainbow Rose, Misfits' Miscellany, Eunoia Review, The Rusty Nail, Bolts of Silk, The Alarmist, L'Allure des Mots, Dark Matter, Turbulence Magazine, The Milo Review, Carcinogenic Poetry, Jellyfish Whispers, Poetry Pacific,* and *Foliate Oak Literary Magazine.*

MIDGE RAYMOND'S short-story collection, *Forgetting English,* received the Spokane Prize for Short Fiction. Her stories have appeared in *TriQuarterly, American Literary Review, Indiana Review, North American Review, Bellevue Literary Review,* the *Los Angeles Times Magazine, The Lascaux Review,* and many other publications.

BRETT GARCIA ROSE is a writer, software entrepreneur, and former animal rights soldier and stutterer. He is the author of *Noise, Losing Found Things,* and *Ren* (forthcoming). His work has been published in *Sunday Newsday Magazine, The Barcelona Review, Opium, Rose and Thorn, The Battered Suitcase, Fiction Attic, Paraphilia* and other literary magazines and anthologies. His short stories have won the Fiction Attic's Short Memoir Award and been nominated for the Million Writer's Award, Best of the Net, The Pushcart Prize, The Lascaux Prize for Short Fiction, and Opium's Bookmark competition. Rose travels extensively, but calls New York City home.

DAVID SALNER has worked as an iron ore miner, steelworker, machinist and general laborer. His writing appears in current or upcoming issues of *River Styx, North American Review, Atlanta Review, The Moth (Ireland), Saranac Review, Tupelo Quarterly, december,* and *Salmagundi.* His second book is *Working Here* (Rooster Hill Press, 2010).

MARJORIE SAUNDERS'S stories and essays have appeared in *Feminist Studies, Confrontation, The Journal, Skirt,* and others. She lives in Cambridge, Massachusetts.

ASHLEY SHELBY is the author of *Red River Rising: The Anatomy of a Flood and the Survival of an American City.* Her journalism, essays, op/eds, and fiction have been widely published and anthologized. She is the recipient of the Third Coast Fiction Prize, a Sustainable Arts Foundation

Promise Award, a Minnesota State Arts Board Grant, and the William Faulkner Short Fiction Award.

JAMES SILBERSTEIN has an MFA from the University of Southern California. His stories have appeared in *Narrative Magazine*, where they have been recognized in the Top Five of the year and as a finalist for the Winter Story Contest. He lives in Orange County, California.

ROSANNA STAFFA earned her MFA in Fiction from Spalding University. Her work has appeared in *The Baltimore Review*, *Spry Literary Journal*, and elsewhere. Her plays have been staged in Tokyo, New York, Los Angeles, Seattle, and Minneapolis. She is the recipient of a McKnight Advancement Grant, a Jerome Fellowship, and an AT/T On Stage Grant.

ROBIN STRATTON has been a writing coach in the Boston area for almost 20 years. She is the author of *The Revision Process, A Guide for Those Months or Years Between Your First Draft and Your Last*, *On Air* (a National Indie Excellence Book Award finalist), *Of Zen and Men*, *In His Genes*, *Blue or Blue Skies*, and two chapbooks, *Dealing with Men* and *Interference from an Unwitting Species*. Her short work has appeared in *Word Riot*, *63 Channels*, *Antithesis Common*, *Poor Richards Almanac(k)*, and many others. She is a three-time Pushcart nominee and presently serves as editor of Boston Literary Magazine.

ALEXANDER WEINSTEIN is the Director of The Martha's Vineyard Institute of Creative Writing (mvicw.com). His fiction and translations have appeared in *Cream City Review, Notre-Dame Review, Pleiades, PRISM International, Rio Grande Review, Salamander, Sou'Wester, World Literature Today, Zone 3*, and other journals. His fiction has been awarded The Lamar York Prize, The Gail Crump Prize, and appears in the anthology *2013 New Stories from the Midwest*. He is a professor of Creative Writing at Siena Heights University, and a lecturer at the University of Michigan.

LEE WRIGHT'S play, "Haint Blue," won the grand prize at the Chattanooga Theatre Centre's 2008 Festival of New Plays. His short stories have appeared or are forthcoming in *Metal Scratches, Literary Juice, Apocrypha and Abstractions, The Journal of Compressed Creative Arts, Eunoia Review, Word Riot, Danse Macabre*, and others.

89113923R00190

Made in the USA
Columbia, SC
17 February 2018